MW00851036

# INSIGHTS
## INTO FUNCTIONAL TRAINING
*PRINCIPLES, CONCEPTS, AND APPLICATION*

# INSIGHTS
## INTO FUNCTIONAL TRAINING
### *PRINCIPLES, CONCEPTS, AND APPLICATION*

**Chuck Wolf, MS, FAFS**

Foreword by Robert Masson, MD

On Target Publications
Santa Cruz, California

Insights into Functional Training
*Principles, Concepts, and Application*

Chuck Wolf
Foreword by Robert Masson, MD

Chuck Wolf photographs by Charlie Fee, Sideline Photography
Illustrations by Jessica Simms, unless otherwise noted
Chapter Three anatomy photos © Mark Nielsen and Shawn Miller. Used with permission.

Copyright © 2017 Chuck Wolf
Foreword © 2017 Robert Masson

ISBN-13: 978-1-931046-83-1

First printing September 2017

All rights reserved. Printed in the United States of America using recycled paper. No part of this book may be reproduced or transmitted in any form whatsoever without written permission from the author or publisher, with the exception of the inclusions of brief quotations in articles or reviews.

On Target Publications

P O Box 1335
Aptos, California 95001 USA

*otpbooks.com*

Library of Congress Cataloging-in-Publication Data

Names: Wolf, Chuck, 1953- author.
Title: Insights into functional training : principles, concepts and application / Chuck Wolf, MS, FAFS ; foreword by Robert Masson, MD.
Description: Santa Cruz, CA : On Target Publications, [2017] I Includes index.
Identifiers: LCCN 2017001349 I ISBN 9781931046831 (pbk.)
Subjects: LCSH: Kinesiology. I Human mechanics.
Classification: LCC QP303 .W65 2017 I DDC 612.7/6--dc23

LC record available at https://lccn.loc.gov/2017001349

# CONTENTS

**Lord Alfred Tennyson from *Ulysses***

*Tho' much is taken, much abides; and tho'*

*We are not now that strength which in old days*

*Moved earth and heaven, that which we are, we are;*

*One equal temper of heroic hearts,*

*Made weak by time and fate, but strong in will*

*To strive, to seek, to find, and not to yield.*

# FOREWORD

Chuck Wolf continues to do amazing work in understanding the limits of human performance while emphasizing injury prevention, biomechanics, and a philosophy that proudly proclaims that the sum of human performance is bigger than the individual components.

I have worked with Chuck for years and he has taught me that the limits to the recovery capabilities of my micro-reconstruction patients lay in the foundation of their total performance. I am always reminded that the better my surgical procedures solve intervertebral joint dysfunction and with less trauma, the more the limits of human recovery are tested.

His time-tested, simple, and honest evaluation and performance principles, continue to lead the way toward a better understanding of human performance both before and after injury. His thoughtful and meaningful concepts have given me a broader and bolder understanding of the value of less traumatic surgical techniques and have given countless patients the optimization of recovery that previously was not possible in the field of complex spinal reconstruction and orthopedics at large.

I strongly recommend the journey of better understanding the mission and concepts presented here as you start your own quest to chase successful wellness and recovery strategies for your clients and patients as they seek to maximize their own version of human performance.

**ROBERT MASSON, MD**
PRESIDENT, NEUROSPINE INSTITUTE
ORLANDO, FLORIDA

# PREFACE

*"The whole is greater than the sum of its parts."*

~ ARISTOTLE

---

Professionals in fitness, physical therapy, and sports performance—*you*—are enactments of the balance of nature as we attempt to create environments for the body, spirit, and soul. Whether the enactment is from a position to promote freedom from illness or injury, to promote the healing process from injured tissue, or attempting to facilitate the highest level of performance, you are attempting to create the environment for optimal health and wellbeing.

Creating the environment for human success is based on concepts derived from the scientific principles to promote improved functional outcomes. The term "concept" is defined as *a plan or intention, a thought process based on the general principles or truths that exist.*

Writing this book has been a process of taking complex principles and transitioning them into a simpler concept to promote improved function.

There are many perspectives to bring about improved health and wellbeing. Some do extremely well, while others are highly scrutinized. They can all become tools in a deep toolbox when based on the principles of movement.

In this book, I do not promote or criticize any approaches to corrective exercise, sports performance, or rehabilitative strategies. We will instead discuss the principles of movement that can help as a tool to enhance the health of the human body.

My intention is to discuss complex principles, while writing in a way that is easy to comprehend. As a result, you will be able to apply the information to produce positive outcomes to promote wellness, improved performance, and enrichment to the human ecosystem.

This book is organized in a progressive fashion. First, we discuss the principles and characteristics of efficient human movement. We will then delve into the joint-by-joint approach to movement within a three-dimensional environment.

The chapter on functional anatomy is not similar to a traditional anatomy textbook. Instead, we will cover the most common myofascial tissue trainers, physical therapists, and sports coaches discuss. The approach compares the *anatomical anatomy* to *functional anatomy*. It is to be used as a quick reference to view the three-dimensional action of these muscles.

Flexibility Highways has been a deep passion of mine for the last 20 years. The six Flexibility Highways described in Chapter Five involve the six cardinal pathways in which I view movement. These movement pathways relate to the fascial connections that involve the tissues forming an integrated relationship within those fascial lines.

The chapter *Blending Tradition with Functional Integrated Training* is where my strategies blend movement principles into conceptual applications.

Exercise and movement strategies are an art based on science determined by the limitations, compensations, and idiosyncrasies of those we serve. The programming chapters are really a hybrid of not only the giants in the fitness, rehabilitation, and sporting worlds, but also include a blend of concepts from my years of practice.

The impetus for this book lies in the chapter called Pre-programming Insights. I have been blessed to work with thousands of clients and patients throughout my career. Many times, I felt they were my living labs who allowed me to try applications of techniques. I wish I could say all were successful; however, that is not the case.

Success is not only derived from positive outcomes, but also from the lessons learned from conceptual applications that were not effective. I was able to learn from those less-than-effective moments and have built that education into the book you are about to read.

*Preprogramming Insights* are lessons learned through repetitive-scenario concepts and the associated applications to improve the function of the client based on the usual principles that should have been present but were not. Applying these concepts to create an environment for success is our goal.

Many of the insights in that chapter are based on strategies that *did* prove to be fruitful, maybe even lucky. When luck hits more than once in similar situations, this then becomes a useful conceptual application.

My goal here is to give back to a field I love. It has given me so much and has deeply fulfilled me. If sharing my passion helps other movement professionals now and in the future, I have done my job.

Thank you for taking the time to read this book. I hope you enjoy it and find it useful.

To your good health!

**CHUCK WOLF**

# CHAPTER ONE

# INSIGHTS INTO FUNCTIONAL TRAINING: PRINCIPLES, CONCEPTS, AND APPLICATION

*"Practice isn't the thing you do once you're good.*
*It is the thing you do that makes you good."*

~ M A L C O L M   G L A D W E L L ,   O U T L I E R S :   T H E   S T O R Y   O F   S U C C E S S

---

The human body is an interdependence of one system upon others necessary for a successful environment as a whole. The circulatory system depends on the respiratory system to deliver rejuvenated processes. The digestive system must nourish each cell, yet must be dependent upon the cardiorespiratory system for that nourishment, as well as remove the waste byproducts the body produces. The nervous system is the supreme regulator of all these interdependent, interactive processes.

No muscle works in isolation or in a single plane of motion. There is a synergistic relationship in all efficient and effective movement. The body moves in a series of chain reactions that are tri-plane in nature and dependent upon the neighboring muscles to share the load and deflect the direct actions on any one muscle. We cannot perform even a simple task, such as picking up a pencil from the floor, by one muscle in any part of the body, but instead are dependent upon the chain reaction and cooperation of the adjacent muscle groups.

"Function" has become a universal term in fitness and healthcare, yet it has never been defined with specific criteria or litmus tests to describe what function is or does.

Likewise, describing human motion has been a complicated, intricate process as it relates to movement.

While the study of human function is an evolving and continuous process, comprehension of function will help you view movement and actions from an entirely different perspective that will lead toward a paradigm shift for your future program design.

The main purpose of *Insights Into Functional Training: Principles, Concepts, and Application* is the development of consistent skills based on human movement and to enhance function through creative latitude while adding new tools to your productive toolbox.

Leading fitness professionals study functional anatomy and understand how motion is a product of the cause and effects of movement, limitations, compensations, and the resultant actions. This is vastly different yet related to the anatomical or textbook anatomy, as opposed to functional anatomy. The excellent information in these texts provides great knowledge of muscles and joint actions in an isolated mode, yet the understanding of functional anatomy better enlightens us to the integrated actions of pure human motion.

As Thomas Myers states in his book *Anatomy Trains (2nd Edition)*:

*"The traditional mechanistic view of anatomy, as useful as it has been, has objectified rather than humanized our relationships to our insides."*

Functional anatomy reveals how the chain reaction of adjacent and sometimes distant muscle and joint actions impacts the resultant human movement. Myers adds:

*"...whatever else they may be doing individually, muscles also influence functionally integrated body-wide continuities..."*

Based on an understanding of the continuous thread of connective tissue, adjacent muscles, and soft tissue, you can create a thought process that views motion and begins to ask the very important questions of *what?...how?... when?...why?*

- *WHY does this action transform into this movement pattern?*
- *WHY are there symptoms?*
- *WHAT is causing them?*
- *HOW can a change in body angle or reach create the chain reaction to enhance function or activities?*
- *HOW or WHY can I manage movement reactions?*

The ability to address these concepts will transform your career and help you become a manager of efficient and effective movement with a valuable, reasoned thought process and subsequent assessment skills. This will help you become a program design expert who can impact the cause of a symptom rather than address the symptom itself—with a focus on the function, not the complaint.

## WE ARE NOT ISLANDS UNTO OURSELVES

"Integrated" is the essential concept here. "Integrated" in the fitness professional model involves *the understanding of incorporated motion from the ground up, and from the top down.*

It is equally important for you to integrate a team of practitioners that synergistically enhances function and quality of life. The integrated, multidisciplinary approach to working with clients means you will develop relationships with other healthcare professionals such as chiropractors, massage therapists, physical therapists, athletic trainers, exercise physiologists, dietitians, family practice physicians, orthopedic surgeons, neurosurgeons, and podiatrists.

The integration of the special skills of these professionals creates a team approach that can then view function, symptoms, health-related issues, and, when necessary, can refer to the medical community. Additionally, having a multidisciplinary team encourages dialogue with other healthcare personnel and ultimately improves the quality of life of the client.

Furthermore, by developing an integrated team of health practitioners, your referral base inherently grows.

## THE INTRIGUE OF THE FUNCTIONAL ANATOMY JOURNEY

Understanding ground-based movement involves knowledge of functional and traditional textbook anatomy, factors of how muscles and joints load in a tri-plane manner, individual threshold of symptoms, power, balance, quality of motion, and points of transformation from the loading phase to the unloading phase.

As students of human movement, we understand that all movements, muscles, and joints simultaneously move in each of the three cardinal planes of motion. Influencing an action in one plane of motion will impact the other two planes as well.

With the power of this knowledge, you will be able to identify the individual thresholds of your clients and be able to create programs that allow early successes in the rebuilding process, while encouraging movement to be the relieving remedy to the dysfunction.

The next stepping stone along this journey is the understanding and application of program design, modifications to movement, and strategies to arrive at the art based on the science of movement. Once there, you will learn to improve your clients' function through movement patterns, changes of body angles, reaches, speed, rhythms, dimensions, and use of equipment to your advantage, rather than existing within the limitations of the equipment.

Finally, creative progressions from basic movement patterns to a complex movement-management program will be part of your arsenal.

The role of fitness has been well documented in the scope of health and wellbeing. Moving forward in our current healthcare reform, you can capture this moment and become an integral part of the healthcare continuum.

To stand apart from the competition, you must internalize the same standards of care and expertise expected of the medical community. What level of expertise would you want in a physician if you were to send a family member to him or her? That same standard of care should be expected of those of us in the fitness community.

In most cases, the fitness professional has more contact with a client than the client does with a physician. This allows us to have tremendous impact on our clients' quality of life and wellbeing; however, it also reminds us we have a paramount responsibility to rise to a higher level of competence to meet the needed services.

By understanding functional anatomy, human movement, and the concept that the site of the injury is only a symptom and not necessarily the problem, you will be able to holistically impact the scores of musculoskeletal issues your clients face.

## WHAT IS THE "F" WORD?

The concept of "functional training" has been a part of fitness for more than 25 years. It is often used with various connotations, is seldom understood, and has more random definitions than there are ways to work the core, whatever that means.

When speaking at conferences, I frequently ask, "Who does functional training?" Most of the attendees raise their hands, but when I ask what functional means, few answer, as there has never been a unifying concept of "functional."

We often hear that "function" is *doing an activity, exercise, or movement pattern that replicates daily living, or that it is a movement pattern that will allow someone to move better.* Frequently, this is a response similar to *an activity that will improve a person's goal to be better at a particular sport.*

Sometimes, the answer is *working in three planes of motion.*

Is there something common among the answers that can identify if a movement pattern is functional? Rarely. Usually people do not know if the programs they have created are functional.

This is the crux of the matter: *We have not identified function as it relates to movement.*

I have visited numerous facilities and watched many trainers working with their clients. Often there does not seem to be a purpose or progression of a program. It is more of a display of the trainer's ability to grind a client into submission.

The idea of "function" has become synonymous with *cool-looking movements,* but does not take into account how clients move, and why they move the way they do. We have taken the concept of purpose and turned it into a circus. There are so many perceptions of "functional training" that many of us have come to despise the words. It has turned into the "F" word, used foolishly, without any unifying concepts to define whether a movement or program is functional in nature.

There are ways to identify if a program, exercise, or movement pattern is functional. Initially, a client presents a certain goal or desire to a trainer. This might be weight loss, increased stamina, improved tone, to reduce the symptoms of an injury, or a number of other reasons.

These are legitimate reasons—these are their goals—yet the trainer needs to delve further to discover why each client has a goal in mind. For instance, if a client wants to lose weight, you must discover why the person feels the need to lose weight and what the person perceives the target weight to be.

This is important for a variety of reasons: Is the target weight a realistic goal? How much time does the client believe it will take to reach that goal? What other measures will the person do to attain that goal—dietary changes, activities when away from you, other psychosocial measures to implement change?

If the person wants increased muscle mass, you should ask why, as this not only gives both you and the client a vision, but you can then also understand the motivating factors that drive those desires.

This builds a relationship that strengthens the bond between you and the client, and also sets a common reality as well.

## WANTS VERSUS NEEDS

As trainers, we must not stop there. We must listen to the client's *wants*, but being hired to enhance a person's quality of life, we must also assess the *needs*.

This is where a comprehensive health history profile and gait-and-motion analysis are beneficial for a complete match of the person's wants and needs.

For example, I have worked with clients who play golf who want to relieve back pain, even though they have already gone through physical therapy with limited success. They state their discomfort has decreased, but they still have a nagging back tightness or pain…and they also want to improve the golf game.

An extensive review of one client's health history uncovered a grade-three ankle sprain about five years prior to the back pain. A gait-and-motion analysis showed the injured ankle had not recaptured the range of motion he had prior to the injury. This impacted his foot function and created a compensation that caused tightness in the same-side hip, and discomfort in the region on the same side above his iliac crest.

The gait-and-motion analysis showed a need we would have to address or it would impact his desire of reducing back discomfort and improving his golf game. When he saw the difference in the unaffected foot and its ankle mobility compared with the affected foot-and-ankle complex, he was astonished that he had never noticed it, and wondered how it might have impacted him in later years.

In this case, it was easy to help him understand the matching of his wants to his needs.

Yet, in other cases you may not have the opportunity to explain the importance of addressing the need, as the client may not want to hear it or care to understand the "why." This is where it is necessary for you to appreciate the learning style and personality of each client and still be able to blend *the wants* with *the needs* to create a successful program. The wants and needs may not coincide, but there must be a subliminal way for you to blend these in order to have a positive impact on the person's quality of life.

We'll cover the gait-and-motion analysis in Chapter Eight, page 123 and you'll find a copy of the health history we use at Human Motion Associates in Appendix Five, page 223.

Next, let's delve into the criteria that makes a program or movement fit into the purpose of function.

## CHARACTERISTICS OF HUMAN MOTION— BRINGING REALITY TO FUNCTION

There are unifying concepts that identify when a movement pattern or program is functional in nature. Prior to starting a program we must know the roadmap of our clients and understand their limitations, compensations, and idiosyncrasies, which we can gain through a gait-and-motion analysis. Once we have established that, we can create a program based on the characteristics of human motion.

We can describe the characteristics of functional human motion as the following:

- *Eccentric before concentric*
- *Go opposite first*
- *Strength in numbers*

- *Muscles are stabilizers*
- *Muscles react to ground forces*
- *In motion, think distal bone first*
- *In the spine, think proximal bone first*

## ECCENTRIC BEFORE CONCENTRIC

The eccentric quality of muscle function is critical for efficient and effective movement. The downward pull of gravity and the impact of ground reaction forces has a three-dimensional effect that we need to decelerate and control in order to produce useful work.

Books teach us that "eccentric contractions" are *muscles lengthening while contracting*. However, that description lacks the three-dimensional quality required to perform the work.

In human motion, "eccentric loading" is *the preloading of action*. The lengthening action of a muscle during eccentric loading is best described when the muscle is lengthening, stretching, decelerating movement, absorbing the forces of gravity, and storing energy before unloading that energy. Anytime the need arises to control or decelerate movement, such as standing up or crouching to prepare to take flight in a jump, the soft tissue—muscle and fascia—must lengthen to decelerate the preparatory action.

Interestingly, eccentric action is a passive response that does not require a conscious effort. For example, lean to your left. As you do, you may notice a passive, subconscious response of the right lateral side—of the obliques, quadratus lumborum, intercostals, latissimus dorsi, lateral gluteal complex—that decelerates the lean so you do not fall to the left.

To further illustrate the passive reaction of eccentric loading, if you are walking in a crowd and get pushed, your myofascial tissue on the opposite side will be recruited to keep you upright and stop you from getting knocked off your feet. This recruitment is a subconscious response that occurs without any forethought.

You are subconsciously warding off external forces.

"Concentric contractions," by definition, are *contractions while the muscle is shortening*. However, that basic understanding of this description does not convey the propulsive actions provided by the concentric phase.

Concentric forces during human movement are shortening, acceleration, propulsive, and the unloading of the harnessed energy. Yet movement that only has a strictly concentric emphasis, such as seen in traditional methods of training, is inefficient and often leads to overuse injury.

Research by Stan Lindstedt et al in his review, "Do muscles function as locomotor springs?" in the *Journal of Experimental Biology* (2002), shows that eccentric contractions allow a muscle to store between three to nine times more energy than that of concentric contractions. This allows us to harness energy, control momentum, stabilize, and ultimately produce forceful, propulsive movements. Without the eccentric "preload" of muscle action, concentric "unloading" actions are inefficient, weak, and ineffective.

## GO OPPOSITE FIRST

When I was in my youth, I recall watching professional wrestling and being amused when a wrestler ran away from his opponent, slammed into the ropes, and was recoiled or catapulted back toward his rival to gain more momentum for a forceful assault. The wrestler initiating this attack went opposite of his intended target.

The physiologic action of "go opposite first" forces us to view action from a different perspective. In a functional action, there is a brief instant causing an action to go opposite first for the sake of efficiency.

For example, in the act of jumping, the desire may be to jump up as high as possible. However, to attain this goal, the body must first go downward. The downward action causes the musculature to decelerate the forces of gravity and preload nearly all muscles, harness the stored or potential energy during the eccentric action of the muscles, and then unload that stored energy during the concentric, propulsive phase of launching upward.

The downward deceleration causes a multitude of chain reactions from forefoot abduction, subtalar joint abduction, calcaneal eversion, ankle dorsiflexion, tibial internal rotation, knee flexion, abduction, and internal rotation; then hip flexion, adduction, and internal rotation; and finally spinal flexion—all designed to go opposite of the intended direction to create an efficient and effective movement pattern. Please refer to Photo 1.1.

*To efficiently jump up, the body must go down first. In the action of loading, the ankle dorsiflexes and the knee and hip flex. This lengthens the calf group, quadriceps, gluteal complex, hamstrings, and erector spinae. The eccentric loading of the tissues decelerates the triple flexion as the body goes into the loading phase.*

**PHOTO 1.1 PREPARING TO JUMP**

## STRENGTH IN NUMBERS

Force transmission through myofascial tissue to the bones and joints must be transferred through the muscle fibers, capsules, and tendons. However, in early studies, this was related through isolated tissue, while recent dissections clearly delineate no clear boundaries of these tissues, but instead show an integrated matrix of tissue.

In 2007, the work *Epimuscular myofascial force transmission between antagonistic and synergistic muscles can explain limitation in spastic paresis* by Peter Huijing, PhD, demonstrated that muscles transmit up to 40% of their contraction force into the tendon via fascial connections into other adjacent muscles.

## MUSCLES ARE STABILIZERS

In isolation, muscles become force producers by concentrically contracting. Our traditional program design trained muscles in an isolated, force-producing method, yet when viewing movement, we realize muscles are dependent upon other regions to accomplish efficient work. Isolated muscle action is virtually the opposite of the true action of muscles in the early phases of integrated motion.

When viewing muscle action during upright motion, imagine watching the activity from under a glass floor. When we see the foot hit the ground and the tibia moving over the foot, the hip moving ahead of the tibia, the rotational aspects, lateral motion, and the forward and backward sway of the hips and torso, it would be quickly apparent that no single muscle created those actions.

Additionally, no muscle concentrically contracts to cause motion. Rather, the muscles are lengthening to control the momentum, to stabilize the joints and harness the energy, and then there is a synergistically concentric instant as the body moves slightly ahead of the foot or when the distal segment is slightly behind the proximal segment of the kinetic chain.

When muscles are concentrically doing propulsive, isolated action, they are doing the work. However, when muscles are controlling tri-plane motion, the proximal segments move over the distal segments, and the muscles elongate to stabilize the joints and movement and are acting involuntarily.

## MUSCLES REACT TO GROUND-REACTION FORCES

Changing ground effects, firm surfaces, undulations, soft surfaces, or unstable surfaces cause the foot to react, setting off a series of chain reactions through the musculoskeletal system. Generally speaking, the more unstable the surface, the greater the eccentric loading to control stability. Please refer to Photo 1.2 and the discussion of Newton's 3rd Law.

**PHOTO 1.2 NEWTON'S CRADLE**

*This classic Newton's Cradle photo demonstrates Newton's 3rd Law that tells us for every action, there is an equal and opposite reaction. As one ball bearing crashes into the line of ball bearings, the one on the opposite end will move away from the group. Likewise, when the foot hits the ground with a certain amount of force, the body will absorb an equal amount of force resonating from the ground.*

## IN MOTION AWAY FROM THE SPINE, THINK DISTAL BONE FIRST

The description of movement away from the spine is based on the relative position of the distal bone to the proximal bone. For instance, if a person moves the left leg across the midline of the body, the action is left hip adduction as shown in Photo 1.3.

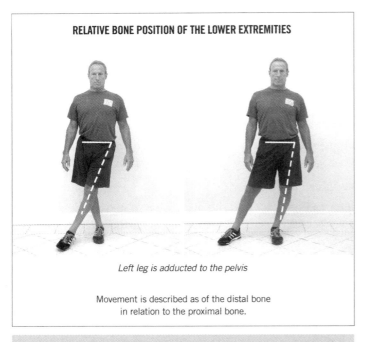

**PHOTO 1.3 RELATIVE BONE POSITION OF THE LOWER EXTREMITIES**

If the person now places more weight on the left side while shifting to the left and positions the hip lateral to the femur, it is still hip adduction. In both cases, the femur—the distal lower bone—is medial or adducted to the pelvis—the proximal upper bone.

## IN THE SPINE, THINK PROXIMAL BONE FIRST

Describing relative spinal position is based on the proximal segment to the distal segment. If a person is standing facing forward and turns the head to the left, the proximal segments move farther to the left in relation to the distal segment. This is left cervical rotation.

However, if the person steps forward with the right leg and turns the shoulders to the right while reaching with the arms to the right, the distal segments have rotated farther to the right than the proximal segments of the cervical spine. Using the principle, "in the spine, think proximal

bone first," the proximal vertebral segment is left rotated in relation to the distal segments. Therefore, this is still considered left rotation of the cervical spine.

The same principle applies to the thoracic and lumbar regions of the spine. Compare the positions of the head to the body in both pictures in Photo 1.4.

**PHOTO 1.4 RELATIVE POSITION OF THE SPINE**

This is a difficult concept. Stop for a minute to review the text and images, and then stand up to recreate the positions to make sure you understand the movement principle of proximal bone relationship to the distal bone.

## ISOLATED INTEGRATION OF JOINTS

To understand this work, you must understand the chain reactions that occur in joints during various aspects of motion. This is the basis of what we will be covering in this book.

Additionally, you then must extrapolate the impact that motion has on other joint structures and muscle actions. This will give you an integrated knowledge of adjacent structures and the application of normal function and also dysfunction, cumulative compensation, and possible mechanisms for injury.

Figure 1.1 displays the tri-plane reaction occurring in the hip, knee, ankle, and foot and is based upon the original movement grid by Gary Gray. This is the foundation and roadmap of the reactions from the foot through the hip. Thorough comprehension of this illustration will help you understand the normal reactions and will provide a rationale for adding changes in body angles and reaches to impact specific movement patterns.

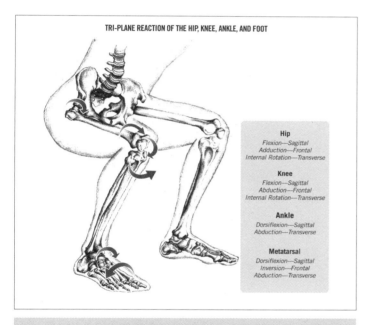

TRI-PLANE REACTION OF THE HIP, KNEE, ANKLE, AND FOOT

**Hip**
*Flexion—Sagittal*
*Adduction—Frontal*
*Internal Rotation—Transverse*

**Knee**
*Flexion—Sagittal*
*Abduction—Frontal*
*Internal Rotation—Transverse*

**Ankle**
*Dorsiflexion—Sagittal*
*Abduction—Transverse*

**Metatarsal**
*Dorsiflexion—Sagittal*
*Inversion—Frontal*
*Abduction—Transverse*

**FIGURE 1.1 TRI-PLANE REACTION OF THE HIP, KNEE, ANKLE, AND FOOT**

The addition of modifications and the reactions to them is the essential impetus for creating the environment to correct limitations and the resulting compensations—and ultimately to enhance performance.

## ISOLATION VERSUS ADAPTABILITY

To help define function or integrated movement, we must develop consistency in the description of human motion. In its most simplistic form, functional movement patterns do not require the equipment settings found on selectorized equipment, and, in fact, are often hindered by them.

Functional training is more lifelike and inherently has adaptability that these weight machines do not have.

Function involves an integrated approach rather than an isolated one. Instead, we must take into account the impact of gravity and ground-reaction forces, control of mass and momentum, and consider how the proprioceptive system will be stimulated. Functional training has greater movement variability than what we find in the limitations of gym-based weight machines.

Think of the principles of movement as more like a cascade or domino effect of reactions creating an efficient movement, rather than an isolated action. In this sense, each motion of the movement is an objective response to the person's individual make-up instead of the subjective environment of an exercise machine.

For example, when using a selectorized leg press, each person using the machine gets into the unit, with the hip joint placed at the point of the axis of rotation on the machine and the feet on the foot pad before commencing the press. But when we perform a squat or a lunge, we can select the foot placement in a narrow or wide stance, evenly or in an asymmetrical or staggered stance, in addition to having the feet in a long, short, or even stride length apart.

Additionally, we do not have to worry about being aligned with the machine's axis of rotation or any other lab-like, artificial setting. The body moves through a natural environment, must control the impact of gravity and ground-reaction forces, and control its own mass and momentum. In these surroundings, the body's proprioceptive system reacts more like a real-life situation than an artificial, machine-like setting.

As you consider these concepts, you will only be limited by your creativity in developing programs rather than the constraints of machine-like equipment. An astute trainer can implement effective training programs based on the movement profile of each client and can often perform it in an empty room or an open field without being dependent on equipment.

Gravity, mass, momentum, and bodyweight are always present. We can use these elements efficiently and effectively in our programming.

CHAPTER TWO

# A THREE-DIMENSIONAL JOINT-BY-JOINT APPROACH TO MOVEMENT

*"We work because it is a chain reaction,
each subject leads to the next."*

~ CHARLES EAMES

A concept recently permeated the fitness, sports performance, and rehabilitation fields describing the body and its movement as a series of alternating joint levels of mobility-stability-mobility patterns. This systematized arrangement of movement idea is good, but the common description of it was incomplete. The simplistic version looked at motion in one dimension, when in reality every muscle and joint works in three planes of motion. There must be an adequate range of motion in all three planes to allow an efficient, economical, and successful chain reaction of synchronized movement.

In this section, we will discuss the principles and concepts of movement, expression of relative motion of joints, basic foot mechanics, and will then delve into the lower extremity, knee, and hip. Later, we will explore the complexity of the lumbar and thoracic spine and of the shoulder girdle.

## DISTAL AND PROXIMAL

First, we need to set the premise for our discussion. As covered in the previous chapter, we describe "movement" as *the relationship of bone segments that comprise the joints.* When discussing motion away from the spine, we look at the position of the distal bone in relation to the proximal bone.

Our discussion will begin at the foot, move through the subtalar joint, and proceed up the chain to the cervical spine. However, let's take a few minutes to make sure the concepts of distal and proximal are clear.

For example, in Photo 2.1 we see the open-chain position of hip adduction with the femur medial to the ilium. In Photo 2.2, we also see the closed-chain, integrated position of hip adduction, even though the foot is not moving in space the way it is in an open-chain action.

In July 2002, the late Dr. Mel Siff wrote an article for *PTontheNET* called "Closed Versus Open Kinetic Chain Exercise." In the article, he quoted Dr. Arthur Steindler, who coined the terms "open and closed kinetic chain."

*"We designate an open kinetic chain a combination in which the terminal joint is free. A closed kinetic chain, on the other hand, is one in which the terminal joint meets with some considerable external resistance which prohibits or restrains its free motion." ~ Kinesiology of the Human Body under Normal and Pathological Conditions, Springfield, 1955*

For the rest of the article, visit:
*http://www.ptonthenet.com/articles/Closed-Versus-Open-Kinetic-Chain-Exercise-1692*

In actuality, integrated human movements are a constant alternation of open and closed chain events that produce efficient outcomes of a desired task.

In both pictures, the femur—the distal bone—is medial or adducted to the proximal bone, the ilium. For the sake of consistency, "distal" references *any point below a point of attachment*. In this case, the femur is below the ilium.

"Medial" refers to *any point closer to the midline* from a referenced starting point. Here, the femur is closer to the midline of the body as related to the ilium.

In the spine, however, the description of "spinal movement" is *the proximal bone in relation to the distal bone*.

In Photo 2.3, we see rotation of the cervical spine to the left with the chin somewhat over the left shoulder. The proximal segments of the cervical spine are rotated farther left than the distal cervical segments.

**PHOTO 2.1 HIP ADDUCTION, OPEN CHAIN**

**PHOTO 2.3 C-SPINE ROTATION TO LEFT, OPEN CHAIN**

When viewing the integrated action as shown in Photo 2.4, there is still left cervical rotation even though the body is rotated right—the proximal cervical segments are left of the distal segments.

**PHOTO 2.2 HIP ADDUCTION, CLOSED CHAIN**

**PHOTO 2.4 C-SPINE ROTATION TO LEFT, CLOSED CHAIN**

*In Photo 2.4, the lower segment of the cervical spine and the thoracic spine are rotated right. However, the proximal segments are rotated to the relative left to the distal segments. Therefore, this is still left cervical rotation.*

## UNDERSTANDING THE SYNERGISTIC RELATIONSHIP FOR MOVEMENT EFFICIENCY

Historically, the majority of exercise training programs have been created in an isolated environment, such as machines in a gym. There are benefits to isolation in training, such as hypertrophy development or to increase isolated strength. These issues are necessary, especially considering a person who is rehabilitating an injury or a postsurgical issue.

However, when we use an isolated movement pattern, it is concentric in nature, in one plane of motion, and is isolated. You can readily see this as opposite of how the body actually moves as described in the earlier section, *Characteristics of Human Motion* beginning on page 14.

Functional, efficient movement is eccentric before concentric, is a tri-plane action, and integrated for successful movement. It is not isolated.

Next, you will see a diagram showing the integrated, synergistic reactions that occur in normal, healthy movements when loading the musculoskeletal system. As you can see, all joints move in three planes of motion. This is the roadmap to keep in mind as you observe a person's gait or during a motion analysis. It is a roadmap you can use to create an environment for a client's success, as these reactions must transpire to allow optimal, efficient motion.

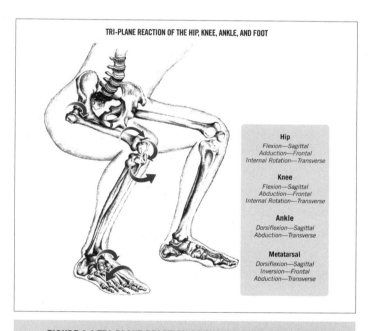

TRI-PLANE REACTION OF THE HIP, KNEE, ANKLE, AND FOOT

**Hip**
*Flexion—Sagittal*
*Adduction—Frontal*
*Internal Rotation—Transverse*

**Knee**
*Flexion—Sagittal*
*Adduction—Frontal*
*Internal Rotation—Transverse*

**Ankle**
*Dorsiflexion—Sagittal*
*Abduction—Transverse*

**Metatarsal**
*Dorsiflexion—Sagittal*
*Inversion—Frontal*
*Abduction—Transverse*

**FIGURE 1.1 TRI-PLANE REACTION OF THE HIP, KNEE, ANKLE, AND FOOT**

There must be adequate range of motion in all three planes to allow an efficient, economical, and successful chain reaction of synchronized movement. There is a predominance of a particular plane of motion in each joint. However, we still expect the presence of the other two cardinal planes of motion during any integrated, functional movement.

For example, the knee moves predominantly in the sagittal plane. But, consider again the principle of motion away from the spine, where movement is defined as the distal bone in relation to the proximal bone. Under normal, healthy conditions, as the knee flexes, the tibia internally rotates, resulting in knee internal rotation. Likewise, as the knee flexes and rotates, the distal end of the tibia is usually lateral to the distal end of the femur. Under these movement principles, the knee is abducted when considering the distal bone in relation to the proximal bone.

Figure 1.1 shows the concomitant tri-plane actions that occur at each joint, as well as the necessary reactions that must transpire to make all joints and movements successful. Notice how the knee flexes in the sagittal plane, abducts in the frontal plane, and internally rotates in the transverse plane. The majority of anatomy and kinesiology books do not discuss these reactions; they only discuss knee flexion. Take a few minutes to ponder this concept if it is new to you.

Many reactions occur in other regions of the body to allow the knee to have efficient motion. For example, the ankle must dorsiflex for the knee to successfully move.

We will discuss ankle dorsiflexion and the important role it plays in allowing an efficient system to move well when we get to the section on foot function beginning on page 29. For now, we will keep our focus on how the ankle must dorsiflex to allow the knee to flex, abduct, and internally rotate in normal actions.

To get a feel of this, please stand and perform a squat, paying close attention to ankle dorsiflexion. If you have good ankle dorsiflexion, the knee will track somewhere close to over the shoelaces. If you have the ability to achieve this necessary function of the ankle, you should feel a smooth squat action.

Now, attempt the squat again, but this time do not dorsiflex the ankle and do not allow the knee to track over your shoelaces. Most often, people feel awkward and may lose balance; they feel the weight more toward the heels, feel more quadriceps recruitment, and—the biggest compensation—they flex more at the hip. Some feel tension in the low back.

Many people who have had a previous ankle, foot, or calf injury who squat or lunge in this manner are at risk of hip, knee, low back, or sacroiliac joint dysfunction or even injury. We will discuss this in more depth when we explore common limitations, compensations, and injury, beginning on page 137.

Referring back to the earlier movement illustration in Figure 1.1, you will see the necessary chain reaction for optimal performance, whatever that may be:

- *Adequate ankle dorsiflexion must be accompanied by adequate subtalar joint eversion and forefoot abduction to allow the tibia to internally rotate.*
- *This causes the knee to internally rotate, abduct, and flex.*
- *With this successful reaction, the femur will follow the tibia and rotate inward.*
- *As the knee is abducted, it "pulls" the femur, thereby causing the femur to be medial to the ilium.*
- *Following the principle of distal bone in relation to the proximal bone, the femur is now adducted to the ilium, resulting in hip adduction.*
- *Likewise, as the femur moves slightly forward of the ilium, the hip is flexed in the sagittal plane.*
- *As a result, a successful hip action loads the gluteal complex in three planes of motion. The hip is flexed in the sagittal plane, adducted in the frontal plane, and internally rotated in the transverse plane.*

We started this global journey from the foot and ankle complex, through the knee and into the hip. If any component becomes locally limited in motion, it will impact successful global reactions.

Remember, if there is a limitation, it will create a compensation. Compensation often results in an injury or a dysfunctional issue, but that typically is not the *cause* of the problem. It is quite possible—and common—to see the cause of a dysfunction be one or two joint levels away from the site of the compensation or injury.

Therefore, we must look globally prior to looking locally to understand and assess the cause of a problem.

That movement graphic looks complex. To make it more understandable, get in front of a mirror and follow the illustration as you start moving in all planes of motion. Stop in a different position after each movement to analyze each of your joint positions and look at the relationship of the distal bone to the proximal bone.

Once you have internalized these concepts, you will begin to more fully appreciate human movement and be better able to unravel the complexities of each motion. When you understand how the body moves and where the motion is limited rather than where it should be coming from, the possibilities of working with and training clients become endless.

We will expand our explorations into the movement of various regions as we delve into each specific area.

# CHAPTER THREE

# FUNCTIONAL ANATOMY—
# AN EVOLVING PERSPECTIVE

*"Understanding human needs is half the job of meeting them."*

~ A D L A I   E   S T E V E N S O N   I I

---

Ponder the anatomy classes from your schooling—all the impressive and at times overwhelming information, the miraculous dissections, and your long, arduous hours of memorization of tissue names, origins, insertions, and actions.

You may also recall thinking that even though the books say the muscles do certain movements, it did not seem authentic to the athletic reactions or activities you did on a daily basis.

This is because traditional anatomy books and classes teach "anatomical anatomy," which is *the study of the tissues and structure in isolation rather than integration.* This is not to claim that traditional anatomy classes are not beneficial; that is far from the truth. However, muscle function in anatomical anatomy courses is taught using the concept of tissue isolation, one plane of motion, and concentric action first.

You already know that muscle function is the opposite of that: Muscle function is integrated reactions in three planes of motion, with deceleration action coming first.

I often joke, "To understand *functional* anatomy, read a book of textbook anatomy, and do the opposite." This is not to say that you should not study anatomical anatomy. We definitely need to have this knowledge to pass exams, boards, certifications, and equally important, to communicate on a level with others in the fields of fitness and physical therapy, and with those in the medical communities. It

is simply to say that we must also incorporate the study of functional anatomy.

A brief review of the *Characteristics of Human Motion* from Chapter One, page 14, reminds us that muscle and fascial tissue moves through eccentric contraction (loading) before concentric contraction (unloading). The initial reaction is to go opposite of the intended movement.

Additionally, there is strength in numbers; no muscle works in isolation. Rather, the muscles work in a synergistic, integrated reaction to overcome mass, momentum, gravity, and ground-reaction forces.

Muscles stabilize joints and are acted upon. They do not produce force if these principles are applied to control the impacts of mass, momentum, gravity, and ground-reaction forces. The forces are intrinsic as a reaction to the changes of body positions and the impact of the external environment.

This section on functional anatomy could be a book unto itself. However, this is not another anatomy textbook—there are many fine volumes that cover this topic with beautiful photos and explanations of the tissues and systems. Instead, this is a quick reference to access the commonly referred to tissues used in exercise program development.

The following pages are images of muscle tissue, from the ground up, with explanations of their respective actions in all three planes of motion.

The reactions are placed into three phases: phase one "deceleration" (eccentric loading), phase two "transition" (isometric or stabilization), and phase three "acceleration" (concentric unloading). These phases are described from the gait-cycle perspective. They can also be applied to activities such as jumping or running and the associated phases of movement.

When studying each muscle tissue, our tendency is to focus on the information for that particular muscle or groups of muscles. It is important to keep in mind that purposeful, efficient movement is the culmination of a series of reactions of tissues locally and globally.

In other words, think of how other tissues in the body (globally) are reacting to the actions of the tissues in a particular region or location (locally). These make up the integrated, body-wide actions that control the overall movement.

## FEET

Flexor Digitorum Brevis
Abductor Hallucis
Abductor Digiti Minimi
Flexor Hallucis Longus
Flexor Digitorum Longus
Extensor Digitorum Brevis
Extensor Hallucis Longus
Extensor Digitorum Longus

## LOWER EXTREMITY

Tibialis Posterior
Soleus
Gastrocnemius
Peroneal Group
Peroneus Brevis
Peroneus Longus
Peroneus Tertius
Hamstrings
Semimembranosus
Semitendinosus
Biceps Femoris
Quadriceps and Sartorius
Tensor Fascia Lata

## HIP

Adductor Group
Adductor Longus
Adductor Magnus
Adductor Brevis
Pectineus
Gracilis
Abductor and Lateral
    Gluteal Complex
Gluteus Minimus
Gluteus Medius
Piriformis
Gluteus Maximus
Psoas
Iliacus
Quadratus Lumborum

## ABDOMINAL COMPLEX

Rectus Abdominis
External Obliques
Internal Obliques
Transverse Abdominis

## BACK

Erector Spinae
Multifidus Lumborum
Multifidus Cervicis
Multifidus Thoracis
Iliocostalis Lumborum
Thoracis Lumborum
Cervicis Lumborum
Latisimus Dorsi
Trapezius
Rhomboids

## SHOULDER COMPLEX

Levator Scapulae
Supraspinatus
Subscapularis
Infraspinatus
Teres Minor
Deltoid
Pectoralis Major and Minor

## UPPER EXTREMITY

Triceps
Biceps Brachii
Brachialis
Brachioradialis

## MUSCLES OF THE FEET

There is no more of a synergistic nature of muscle tissue than in the foot. The 24 muscles are listed below with the origin and insertion. You will find frequent discussion of the four components of foot function throughout the book.

The loading or pronation is the deceleration phase, when all tissues lengthen to absorb force during calcaneal eversion and forefoot abduction. The transition from pronation to the acceleration or supination phase is when the muscles shorten to lock or close-pack the bones to create a more rigid environment for propulsion.

The following are the muscles affecting foot function.

*Flexor Digitorum Brevis*
*Abductor Hallucis*
*Abductor Digiti Minimi*
*Flexor Hallucis Longus*
*Flexor Digitorum Longus*
*Extensor Digitorum Brevis*
*Extensor Hallucis Longus*
*Extensor Digitorum Longus*

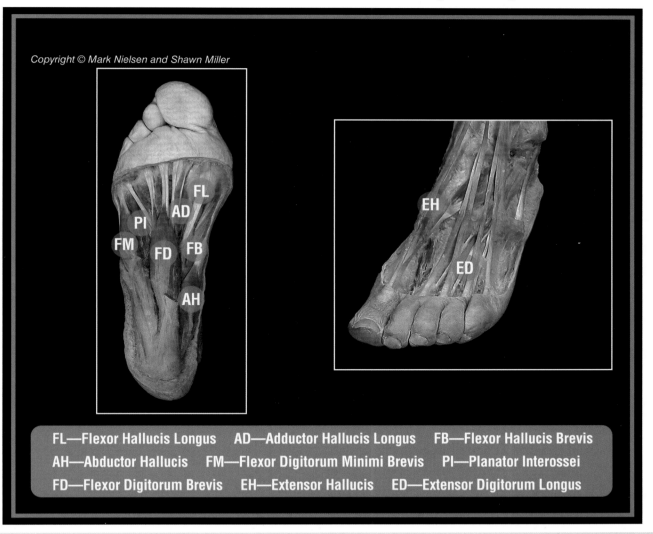

Copyright © Mark Nielsen and Shawn Miller

FL—Flexor Hallucis Longus    AD—Adductor Hallucis Longus    FB—Flexor Hallucis Brevis
AH—Abductor Hallucis    FM—Flexor Digitorum Minimi Brevis    PI—Planator Interossei
FD—Flexor Digitorum Brevis    EH—Extensor Hallucis    ED—Extensor Digitorum Longus

**PHOTO 3.1 THE FOOT**

## FLEXOR DIGITORUM BREVIS

| FUNCTIONAL ACTION | PHASE 1: DECELERATION | PHASE 2: TRANSITION | PHASE 3: ACCELERATION |
|---|---|---|---|
| *SAGITTAL PLANE* | Assists with deceleration of extension of toes two through four from heel strike through toe-off | Foot stabilization | Assists with acceleration of plantar flexion of toes two through four. However, think in terms of relative flexion of the toes prior to heel-off when they begin with deceleration of extension through toe-off. |
| *FRONTAL PLANE* | Foot stabilization in functional activities | Foot stabilization in functional activities | Foot stabilization in functional activities |
| *TRANSVERSE PLANE* | Foot stabilization in functional activities | Foot stabilization in functional activities | Foot stabilization in functional activities |

| | |
|---|---|
| *ORIGIN* | Medial aspect of calcaneal tuberosity and deep surface of the plantar aponeurosis |
| *INSERTION* | Middle phalanx behind flexor digitorum longus |
| *BY THE BOOK* | Flexion of toes two through four |

## ABDUCTOR HALLUCIS

| FUNCTIONAL ACTION | PHASE 1: DECELERATION | PHASE 2: TRANSITION | PHASE 3: ACCELERATION |
|---|---|---|---|
| *SAGITTAL PLANE* | Assists with deceleration of the first metatarsophalange (MTP) | Synergistically assists with great toe stabilization | Assists with deceleration of great toe flexion during heel-off through toe-off |
| *FRONTAL PLANE* | Deceleration of great toe adduction of the first MTP | Synergistically assists with first MTP stabilization | Assists with acceleration of first MTP flexion and abduction during heel-off through toe-off |
| *TRANSVERSE PLANE* | Synergistically assists with first MTP stabilization | Synergistically assists with first MTP stabilization | Synergistically assists with first MTP stabilization during heel-off through toe-off |

| | |
|---|---|
| *ORIGIN* | Flexor retinaculum, medial aspect of calcaneal tuberosity, and deep surface of the plantar aponeurosis |
| *INSERTION* | Medial side of proximal phalanx of the first toe and medial sesamoid bone of the great toe |
| *BY THE BOOK* | Flexion and abduction of the first MTP |

## ABDUCTOR DIGITI MINIMI

| FUNCTIONAL ACTION | PHASE 1: DECELERATION | PHASE 2: TRANSITION | PHASE 3: ACCELERATION |
|---|---|---|---|
| *SAGITTAL PLANE* | Assists with deceleration of fifth toe extension | Assists with fifth toe stability | Assists with acceleration of fifth toe relative flexion after toe-off |
| *FRONTAL PLANE* | Assists with fifth toe adduction | Assists with fifth toe stability | Assists with fifth toe abduction from heel-off through toe-off |
| *TRANSVERSE PLANE* | Dynamic stabilization of the fifth toe | Dynamic stabilization of the fifth toe | Dynamic stabilization of the fifth toe |

| | |
|---|---|
| *ORIGIN* | Inferior calcaneus |
| *INSERTION* | Lateral side of the fifth MTP |
| *BY THE BOOK* | Flexion and abduction of the fifth MTP |

## FLEXOR HALLUCIS LONGUS

| FUNCTIONAL ACTION | PHASE 1: DECELERATION | PHASE 2: TRANSITION | PHASE 3: ACCELERATION |
|---|---|---|---|
| *SAGITTAL PLANE* | Assists with deceleration of great toe extension and ankle eversion at heel strike to mid-stance | Great toe and ankle stability during mid-stance | Assists with deceleration of great toe extension and ankle eversion during heel-off and toe-off |
| *FRONTAL PLANE* | Assists with great toe and foot stability during the entire gait cycle | Assists with great toe and foot stability during mid-stance | Assists with great toe and foot stability |
| *TRANSVERSE PLANE* | Assists with great toe and foot stability during the entire gait cycle | Assists with great toe and foot stability during mid-stance | Assists with great toe and foot stability |

| | |
|---|---|
| *ORIGIN* | Mid-posterior half of fibula |
| *INSERTION* | Distal phalanx of the first MTP on the plantar surface |
| *BY THE BOOK* | Assists in first toe flexion and foot and ankle inversion |

## FLEXOR DIGITORUM LONGUS

| FUNCTIONAL ACTION | PHASE 1: DECELERATION | PHASE 2: TRANSITION | PHASE 3: ACCELERATION |
|---|---|---|---|
| SAGITTAL PLANE | Assists with deceleration of the four lesser toes as the toes reach the ground during heel strike to mid-stance | Synergistically assists with the four lesser toe stabilization | Assists with acceleration of flexion of the four lesser toes |
| FRONTAL PLANE | Assists in deceleration of ankle eversion during heel strike to mid-stance | Foot and ankle stability | Foot and ankle inversion and stability |
| TRANSVERSE PLANE | Foot and ankle stability | Foot and ankle stability | Foot and ankle stability |

| ORIGIN | Posterior middle tibia |
|---|---|
| INSERTION | Distal plantar surface of the lesser four toes |
| BY THE BOOK | Flexion of the four lesser toes and ankle inversion |

## EXTENSOR DIGITORUM BREVIS

| FUNCTIONAL ACTION | PHASE 1: DECELERATION | PHASE 2: TRANSITION | PHASE 3: ACCELERATION |
|---|---|---|---|
| SAGITTAL PLANE | Assists with deceleration of flexion of MTPs two through four | Synergistically assists with stabilization of MTPs two through four | Assists with acceleration of extension of MTPs two through four at heel strike |
| FRONTAL PLANE | Dynamic stabilization of MTPs two through four and assists with deceleration of ankle inversion | Dynamic stabilization of MTPs two through four | Dynamic stabilization of MTPs two through four |
| TRANSVERSE PLANE | Dynamic stabilization of MTPs two through four | Dynamic stabilization of MTPs two through four | Dynamic stabilization of MTPs two through four |

| ORIGIN | Dorsal aspect of calcaneus |
|---|---|
| INSERTION | MTPs two through four |
| BY THE BOOK | Extension of MTPs two through four |

## EXTENSOR HALLUCIS LONGUS

| FUNCTIONAL ACTION | PHASE 1: DECELERATION | PHASE 2: TRANSITION | PHASE 3: ACCELERATION |
|---|---|---|---|
| SAGITTAL PLANE | Assists with deceleration of first MTP extension and ankle plantar flexion | Synergistically assists with first MTP stabilization | Assists with deceleration of first MTP flexion at mid-stance prior to heel-off and toe-off |
| FRONTAL PLANE | Assists in deceleration of ankle eversion | Synergistically assists in first MTP stabilization | Assists in deceleration of ankle inversion |
| TRANSVERSE PLANE | Synergistically assists in first MTP stabilization | Synergistically assists in first MTP stabilization | Synergistically assists in first MTP stabilization |

| | |
|---|---|
| ORIGIN | Anterior fibula and interosseous membrane |
| INSERTION | Dorsal surface of distal phalanx of the first MTP |
| BY THE BOOK | First MTP extension, ankle inversion, and ankle dorsiflexion |

## EXTENSOR DIGITORUM LONGUS

| FUNCTIONAL ACTION | PHASE 1: DECELERATION | PHASE 2: TRANSITION | PHASE 3: ACCELERATION |
|---|---|---|---|
| SAGITTAL PLANE | Assists with deceleration of flexion of MTPs two through five | Synergistically assists with stabilization of MTPs two through four | Assists with deceleration of flexion of MTPs two through four |
| FRONTAL PLANE | Dynamic stabilization of MTPs two through five | Dynamic stabilization of MTPs two through five | Assists in deceleration of ankle inversion |
| TRANSVERSE PLANE | Dynamic stabilization of MTPs two through five | Dynamic stabilization of MTPs two through five | Dynamic stabilization of MTPs two through five |

| | |
|---|---|
| ORIGIN | Lateral tibial condyle, proximal fibula |
| INSERTION | Lateral four lesser toes |
| BY THE BOOK | Extension of MTPs two through five and assists in ankle eversion |

## LOWER EXTREMITY

*Tibialis Posterior*

*Soleus*

*Gastrocnemius*

*Peroneal Group*

*Peroneus Brevis*

*Peroneus Longus*

*Peroneus Tertius*

*Hamstrings*

*Semimembranosus*

*Semitendinosus*

*Biceps Femoris*

*Quadriceps and Sartorius*

*Tensor Fascia Lata*

# TIBIALIS POSTERIOR

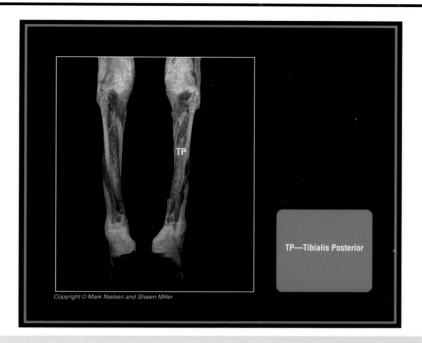

TP

TP—Tibialis Posterior

Copyright © Mark Nielsen and Shawn Miller

PHOTO 3.2 TIBIALIS POSTERIOR

| FUNCTIONAL ACTION | PHASE 1: DECELERATION | PHASE 2: TRANSITION | PHASE 3: ACCELERATION |
|---|---|---|---|
| **SAGITTAL PLANE** | Assists with deceleration of dorsiflexion, assists with subtalar joint deceleration during heel strike through mid-stance | Stabilizes talonavicular joint at mid-stance | Assists with acceleration of plantarflexion during heel-off |
| **FRONTAL PLANE** | Assists with stabilization of the talonavicular joint during mid-stance to heel-off | Stabilizes subtalar joint during mid-stance | Assists subtalar joint supination and inversion just prior to and during heel-off through toe-off. |
| **TRANSVERSE PLANE** | Decelerates tibial internal rotation at heel strike through mid-stance | Stabilizes subtalar joint during mid-stance | Assists with foot inversion during propulsion at heel-off through the swing phase to the heel strike of the next cycle |

| | |
|---|---|
| **ORIGIN** | Posterior proximal tibia and fibula |
| **INSERTION** | Navicular, cuneiform, base of metatarsals two to four |
| **BY THE BOOK** | Plantarflexion, inversion of the ankle |

# SOLEUS

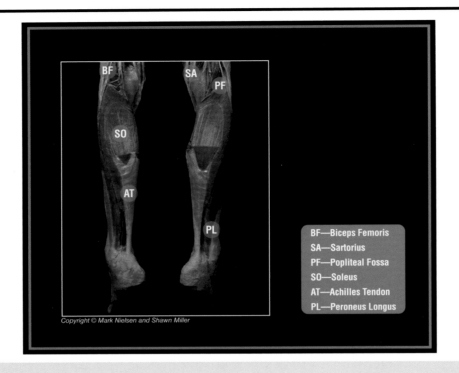

BF—Biceps Femoris
SA—Sartorius
PF—Popliteal Fossa
SO—Soleus
AT—Achilles Tendon
PL—Peroneus Longus

Copyright © Mark Nielsen and Shawn Miller

**PHOTO 3.3 SOLEUS**

| FUNCTIONAL ACTION | PHASE 1: DECELERATION | PHASE 2: TRANSITION | PHASE 3: ACCELERATION |
|---|---|---|---|
| *SAGITTAL PLANE* | Assists in deceleration of ankle dorsiflexion as the tibia moves over the foot | Stabilizes subtalar joint at mid-stance | Assists with ankle plantar flexion and knee extension during heel-off |
| *FRONTAL PLANE* | Assists with subtalar joint pronation from heel strike to mid-stance | Stabilizes subtalar joint at mid-stance | Assists subtalar joint supination as the hip moves over the foot and just prior to heel-off |
| *TRANSVERSE PLANE* | Assists in deceleration of tibial internal rotation from heel strike to mid-stance | Stabilizes subtalar joint at mid-stance | Assists with external rotation of the knee at heel-off through toe-off |

| | |
|---|---|
| *ORIGIN* | Head of fibula and medial border of tibia |
| *INSERTION* | Calcaneus via the achilles tendon |
| *BY THE BOOK* | Plantarflexion |

# GASTROCNEMIUS

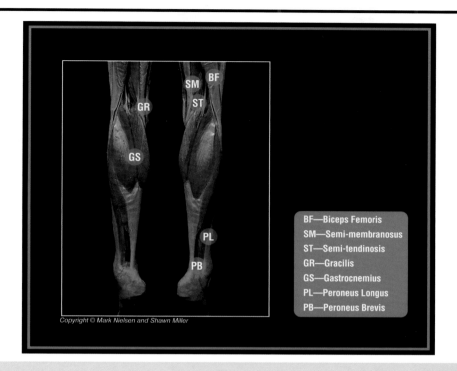

BF—Biceps Femoris
SM—Semi-membranosus
ST—Semi-tendinosis
GR—Gracilis
GS—Gastrocnemius
PL—Peroneus Longus
PB—Peroneus Brevis

Copyright © Mark Nielsen and Shawn Miller

**PHOTO 3.4 GASTROCNEMIUS**

| FUNCTIONAL ACTION | PHASE :1 DECELERATION | PHASE 2: TRANSITION | PHASE 3: ACCELERATION |
|---|---|---|---|
| *SAGITTAL PLANE* | Assists with deceleration of ankle dorsiflexion at heel strike through mid-stance as the hip moves over the foot | Stabilizes subtalar joint and tibio-femoral joint during mid-stance | Assists with knee extension as the hip moves over the foot and the heel is on the ground, and plantarflexion at heel-off to toe-off. |
| *FRONTAL PLANE* | Assists in subtalar joint pronation from heel strike to mid-stance | Stabilizes subtalar joint at mid-stance until prior to heel-off | Assists in acceleration of subtalar joint supination during heel-off through the swing phase until heel strike of the same foot |
| *TRANSVERSE PLANE* | Assists in deceleration of femoral internal rotation from heel strike through mid-stance | Assists with stabilization of the subtalar tibio-femoral joint during mid-stance | Assists in acceleration of external rotation of the knee upon heel-off through the swing phase to heel strike of the next cycle |

| | |
|---|---|
| *ORIGIN* | Lateral and medial femoral condyles |
| *INSERTION* | Calcaneus via the Achilles tendon |
| *BY THE BOOK* | Plantarflexion |

## PERONEAL GROUP

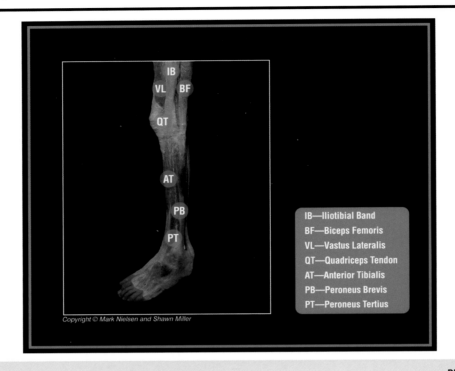

IB—Iliotibial Band
BF—Biceps Femoris
VL—Vastus Lateralis
QT—Quadriceps Tendon
AT—Anterior Tibialis
PB—Peroneus Brevis
PT—Peroneus Tertius

Copyright © Mark Nielsen and Shawn Miller

PHOTO 3.5 PERONEAL GROUP

| FUNCTIONAL ACTION | PHASE 1: DECELERATION | PHASE 2: TRANSITION | PHASE 3: ACCELERATION |
|---|---|---|---|
| SAGITTAL PLANE | Assists with deceleration of ankle dorsiflexion at heel strike through mid-stance | Assists with subtalar joint deceleration during mid-stance just prior to heel-off | Assist with ankle plantarflexion and knee extension at heel-off and toe-off |
| FRONTAL PLANE | Assists with subtalar joint pronation from heel strike through the beginning phase of mid-stance | Assists with stabilization of the subtalar joint in mid-stance | Assists with subtalar joint supination from heel-off through toe-off until heel strike of the next gait cycle |
| TRANSVERSE PLANE | Assists with deceleration of tibial internal rotation at heel strike through mid-stance | Assists with stabilization of the subtalar joint and the first ray | Assists with external rotation of knee during heel-off and toe-off |

| | |
|---|---|
| ORIGIN (PERONEUS LONGUS) | Proximal two-thirds of the lateral fibula |
| INSERTION | Base of the first metatarsal and medial cuneiform |
| BY THE BOOK | Synergistic ankle eversion, assists in plantarflexion |

| ORIGIN (PERONEUS BREVIS) | Distal two-thirds of the lateral fibula |
| --- | --- |
| INSERTION | Fifth metatarsal tuberosity |
| BY THE BOOK | Synergistic ankle eversion, assists in plantarflexion |

| ORIGIN (PERONEUS TERTIUS) | Distal third of the medial fibula and adjacent interosseous membrane (fibers blend with the extensor digitorum longus) |
| --- | --- |
| INSERTION | Fifth metatarsal tuberosity on the medial side of the dorsal surface of the base of fifth metatarsal and down the shaft of the bone |
| BY THE BOOK | Synergistic ankle dorsiflexion, assists in eversion of the foot |

## HAMSTRINGS GROUP

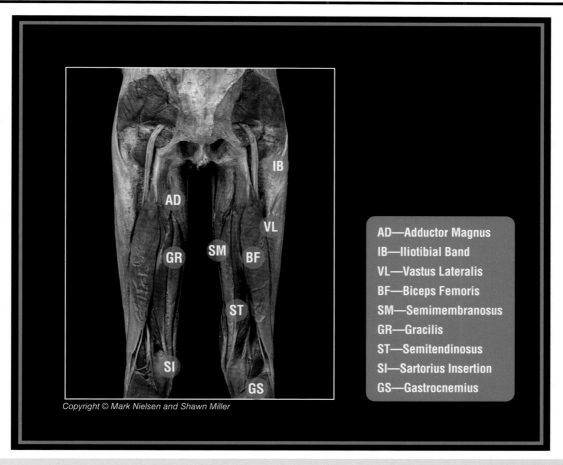

AD—Adductor Magnus
IB—Iliotibial Band
VL—Vastus Lateralis
BF—Biceps Femoris
SM—Semimembranosus
GR—Gracilis
ST—Semitendinosus
SI—Sartorius Insertion
GS—Gastrocnemius

Copyright © Mark Nielsen and Shawn Miller

**PHOTO 3.6 HAMSTRINGS GROUP**

| FUNCTIONAL ACTION | PHASE 1: DECELERATION | PHASE 2: TRANSITION | PHASE 3: ACCELERATION |
|---|---|---|---|
| *SAGITTAL PLANE* | Assists with deceleration of knee extension prior to heel strike; assists with deceleration of posterior pelvic tilt at heel strike | Assists in knee and hip stabilization during mid-stance | Assists with acceleration of knee flexion at heel-off and hip extension at toe-off |
| *FRONTAL PLANE* | Assists in lumbo-pelvic-hip stabilization at heel strike | Assists in knee and hip stabilization during mid-stance | Assists with concentric hip abduction during heel-off through toe-off |
| *TRANSVERSE PLANE* | Assists with deceleration of knee internal rotation during heel strike to mid-stance | Assists in knee and hip stabilization during mid-stance | Assists in knee and hip external rotation during heel-off through toe-off |

| | |
|---|---|
| *ORIGIN—BICEPS FEMORIS SHORT AND LONG HEADS* | Linea aspera of the femur, ischial tuberosity |
| *INSERTION—SHORT AND LONG HEADS* | Fibula head and lateral tibial condyle |
| *BY THE BOOK* | Knee flexion, assists hip extension, tibial external rotation |

| | |
|---|---|
| *ORIGIN—SEMITENDINOSUS* | Ischial tuberosity |
| *INSERTION* | Medial, proximal tibial body |
| *BY THE BOOK* | Knee flexion, assists hip extension, tibial internal rotation |

| | |
|---|---|
| *ORIGIN—SEMIMEMBRANOSUS* | Ischial tuberosity |
| *INSERTION* | Medial tibial condyle |
| *BY THE BOOK* | Knee flexion, assist hip extension, tibial internal rotation |

## QUADRICEPS AND SARTORIUS

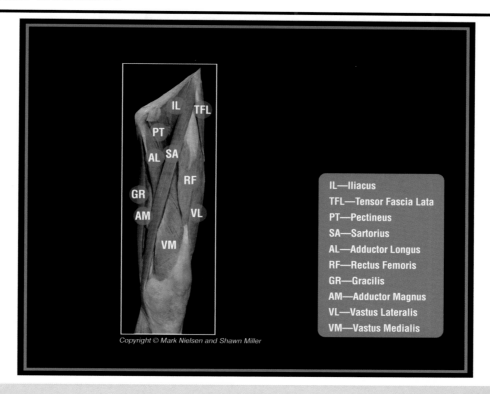

IL—Iliacus
TFL—Tensor Fascia Lata
PT—Pectineus
SA—Sartorius
AL—Adductor Longus
RF—Rectus Femoris
GR—Gracilis
AM—Adductor Magnus
VL—Vastus Lateralis
VM—Vastus Medialis

Copyright © Mark Nielsen and Shawn Miller

**PHOTO 3.7 QUADRICEPS AND SARTORIUS**

## QUADRICEPS

| FUNCTIONAL ACTION | PHASE 1: DECELERATION | PHASE 2: TRANSITION | PHASE 3: ACCELERATION |
|---|---|---|---|
| **SAGITTAL PLANE** | Assists with deceleration of knee flexion during heel strike | Assists with knee and hip stabilization | Assists with deceleration of knee flexion at heel-off and deceleration of hip extension from heel-off through toe-off |
| **FRONTAL PLANE** | Assists with knee adduction during heel strike | Assists with deceleration of knee abduction during mid-stance and hip adduction while stabilizing the knee and hip during mid-stance | Assists with concentric hip abduction during heel-off |
| **TRANSVERSE PLANE** | Assists with deceleration of knee internal rotation during heel strike | Assists in deceleration of knee internal and stabilizing the knee during mid-stance | Assists with knee and hip external rotation during heel-off |

| ORIGIN—RECTUS FEMORIS | Anterior inferior iliac spine (AIIS) |
|---|---|
| INSERTION | Tibial tuberosity via the patellar tendon |
| BY THE BOOK | Knee extension |

| ORIGIN—VASTUS MEDIALIS | Linea aspera of the femur |
|---|---|
| INSERTION | Tibial tuberosity via the patellar tendon |
| BY THE BOOK | Knee extension |

| ORIGIN—VASTUS LATERALIS | Greater trochanter and linea aspera of femur |
|---|---|
| INSERTION | Tibial tuberosity via the patellar tendon |
| BY THE BOOK | Knee extension |

| ORIGIN—VASTUS INTERMEDIUS (NOT VISIBLE IN THE PHOTO BECAUSE IT LIES UNDER THE RECTUS FEMORIS) | Anterior surface of femur |
|---|---|
| INSERTION | Tibial tuberosity via the patellar tendon |
| BY THE BOOK | Knee extension |

## SARTORIUS

| FUNCTIONAL ACTION | PHASE 1: DECELERATION | PHASE 2: TRANSITION | PHASE 3: ACCELERATION |
|---|---|---|---|
| SAGITTAL PLANE | Assists with deceleration of knee flexion at heel strike into mid-stance | Synergistically assists in stabilization of hip extension and knee external rotation at mid-stance | Assists with deceleration of hip extension and external rotation of the knee during heel-off and toe-off |
| FRONTAL PLANE | Assists with deceleration of tibial adduction at heel strike | Synergistically assists in stabilization of hip adduction and knee abduction during mid-stance | Assists in acceleration of tibial adduction as the knee extends during heel-off and toe-off |

| FUNCTIONAL ACTION | PHASE 1: DECELERATION | PHASE 2: TRANSITION | PHASE 3: ACCELERATION |
| --- | --- | --- | --- |
| TRANSVERSE PLANE | Assists with deceleration of tibial external rotation, hip internal rotation at heel strike | Synergistically assists in stabilization of the hip and knee during mid-stance | Assists with acceleration of tibial external rotation and hip external rotation during heel and toe-off |

| ORIGIN—SARTORIUS | Anterior superior iliac spine (ASIS) |
| --- | --- |
| INSERTION | Medial surface of tibia |
| BY THE BOOK | Assists in knee flexion, abduction, external rotation, hip flexion, and external rotation |

# TENSOR FASCIA LATA

| FUNCTIONAL ACTION | PHASE 1: DECELERATION | PHASE 2: TRANSITION | PHASE 3: ACCELERATION |
| --- | --- | --- | --- |
| SAGITTAL PLANE | Assists with deceleration of hip extension as the hip moves over the foot through heel-off and toe-off | Synergistically assists in stabilization of hip | Assists with hip flexion during the swing phase to heel strike |
| FRONTAL PLANE | Assists with deceleration of hip adduction at heel strike | Synergistically assists in stabilization of hip adduction during mid-stance | Assists in acceleration of hip adduction as the knee extends during heel-off and toe-off |
| TRANSVERSE PLANE | Assists with deceleration of tibial external rotation at heel strike and assists with hip internal rotation from heel strike into mid-stance | Synergistically assists in stabilization of the hip and knee during mid-stance | Assists with deceleration of hip external rotation and during heel-off and toe-off |

| ORIGIN—TENSOR FASCIA LATA | Iliac crest, lateral aspect anterior superior iliac spine (ASIS) |
| --- | --- |
| INSERTION | Descends between the two layers of the iliotibial tract to the tibia |
| BY THE BOOK | Assists in hip flexion, abduction, internal rotation, hip flexion |

# HIP

| | | |
|---|---|---|
| *Adductor Group* | *Gracilis* | *Gluteus Maximus* |
| *Adductor Longus* | *Abductor and Lateral Gluteal Complex* | *Psoas* |
| *Adductor Magnus* | *Gluteus Minimus* | *Iliacus* |
| *Adductor Brevis* | *Gluteus Medius* | *Quadratus Lumborum* |
| *Pectineus* | *Piriformis* | |

# ADDUCTOR GROUP

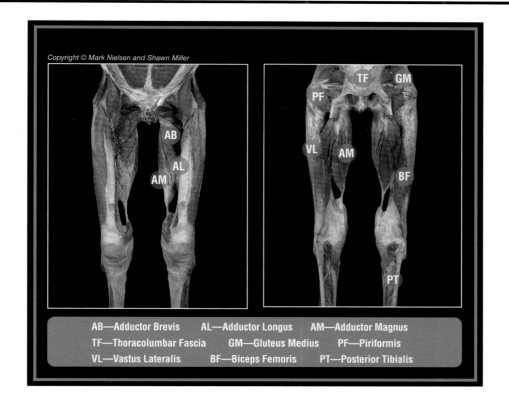

Copyright © Mark Nielsen and Shawn Miller

AB—Adductor Brevis      AL—Adductor Longus      AM—Adductor Magnus
TF—Thoracolumbar Fascia      GM—Gluteus Medius      PF—Piriformis
VL—Vastus Lateralis      BF—Biceps Femoris      PT—Posterior Tibialis

**PHOTO 3.8 ADDUCTOR GROUP**

| FUNCTIONAL ACTION | PHASE 1: DECELERATION | PHASE 2: TRANSITION | PHASE 3: ACCELERATION |
|---|---|---|---|
| *SAGITTAL PLANE* | Assists with lumbo-pelvic-hip complex stabilization, assists in deceleration of hip flexion of the lead leg at heel strike | Assists with lumbo-pelvic-hip complex stabilization in mid-stance | Assists in lumbo-pelvic-hip complex stabilization, assists in deceleration of hip extension of the rear leg through heel-off and toe-off of the gait cycle |
| *FRONTAL PLANE* | Assists with deceleration of hip abduction of the opposite hip | Assists with lumbo-pelvic-hip complex stabilization in mid-stance | Assists in acceleration from hip abduction to hip adduction on the same side |
| *TRANSVERSE PLANE* | Assists with deceleration of hip and knee internal rotation during heel strike | Assists in lumbo-pelvic-hip complex stabilization in mid-stance | Assists in knee and hip external rotation during heel-off |

| ORIGIN—LONGUS | Pubic tubercle |
|---|---|
| INSERTION | Medial linea aspera |
| BY THE BOOK | Assists in concentric hip adduction, flexion, internal rotation |

| ORIGIN—BREVIS | Inferior pubic ramus |
|---|---|
| INSERTION | Pectineal line, medial linea aspera |
| BY THE BOOK | Assists in concentric hip adduction, flexion, internal rotation |

| ORIGIN—MAGNUS | Inferior pubic ramus, ischial tuberosity |
|---|---|
| INSERTION | Adductor tubercle, lateral linea aspera |
| BY THE BOOK | Assists hip adduction and extension |

| ORIGIN—PECTINEUS | Superior pubic ramus |
|---|---|
| INSERTION | Pectineal line of femur between lesser trochanter and linea aspera |
| BY THE BOOK | Assists in hip adduction and internal rotation |

| ORIGIN—GRACILIS | Pubic symphysis and ramus |
|---|---|
| INSERTION | Medial, proximal tibia at pes anserinus tendon |
| BY THE BOOK | Assists in adduction and internal rotation of femur |

# ABDUCTORS AND LATERAL GLUTEAL COMPLEX

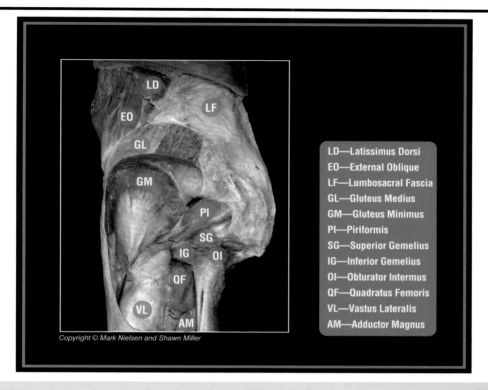

LD—Latissimus Dorsi
EO—External Oblique
LF—Lumbosacral Fascia
GL—Gluteus Medius
GM—Gluteus Minimus
PI—Piriformis
SG—Superior Gemelius
IG—Inferior Gemelius
OI—Obturator Intermus
QF—Quadratus Femoris
VL—Vastus Lateralis
AM—Adductor Magnus

Copyright © Mark Nielsen and Shawn Miller

PHOTO 3.9 LATERAL GLUTEAL COMPLEX

| FUNCTIONAL ACTION | PHASE 1: DECELERATION | PHASE 2: TRANSITION | PHASE 3: ACCELERATION |
|---|---|---|---|
| *SAGITTAL PLANE* | Assists with deceleration of hip flexion at heel strike by way of fascial connection to the gluteus maximus | Assists in hip stabilization during mid-stance by way of fascial connection to the gluteus maximus | Assists acceleration of hip extension from mid-stance through heel-off and toe-off by way of fascial connection to the gluteus maximus |
| *FRONTAL PLANE* | Decelerates hip adduction during heel strike and mid-stance | Assists in stabilizing the hip during mid-stance | Assists in concentric hip abduction during propulsion |
| *TRANSVERSE PLANE* | Assists with deceleration of hip internal rotation during heel strike and knee internal rotation via the iliotibial band during heel strike | Assists in stabilizing the hip and knee via the iliotibial band during mid-stance | Assists in hip external rotation during heel-off. Also contributes to knee external rotation due to the connection of the iliotibial band |

| ORIGIN—GLUTEUS MINIMUS | Under gluteus medius, attached to ilium |
| --- | --- |
| INSERTION | Greater trochanter |
| BY THE BOOK | Hip abduction, internal rotation |

| ORIGIN—GLUTEUS MEDIUS | Attached to ilium between the PSIS and iliac crest |
| --- | --- |
| INSERTION | Greater trochanter |
| BY THE BOOK | Abduction of the leg (femur), anterior fibers: internal rotation; posterior fibers: external rotation |

| ORIGIN—PIRIFORMIS | Anterior surface of sacrum |
| --- | --- |
| INSERTION | Superior greater trochanter |
| BY THE BOOK | Hip external rotation and extension |

# GLUTEUS MAXIMUS

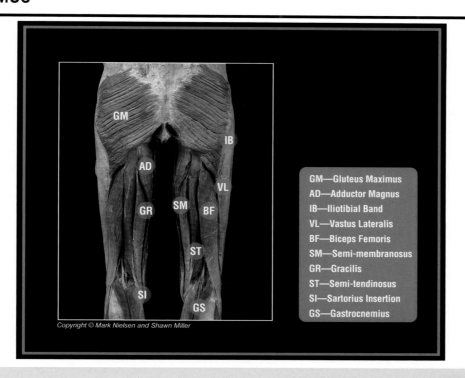

GM—Gluteus Maximus
AD—Adductor Magnus
IB—Iliotibial Band
VL—Vastus Lateralis
BF—Biceps Femoris
SM—Semi-membranosus
GR—Gracilis
ST—Semi-tendinosus
SI—Sartorius Insertion
GS—Gastrocnemius

Copyright © Mark Nielsen and Shawn Miller

**PHOTO 3.10 GLUTEUS MAXIMUS**

| FUNCTIONAL ACTION | PHASE 1: DECELERATION | PHASE 2: TRANSITION | PHASE 3: ACCELERATION |
|---|---|---|---|
| *SAGITTAL PLANE* | Assists with deceleration of hip flexion at heel strike | Assists in hip stabilization during mid-stance | Assists acceleration of hip extension from mid-stance through heel-off and toe-off |
| *FRONTAL PLANE* | Decelerates hip adduction during heel strike and mid-stance | Assists in stabilizing the hip during mid-stance | Assists in concentric hip abduction during propulsion |
| *TRANSVERSE PLANE* | Assists with deceleration of hip internal rotation during heel strike and knee internal rotation via the iliotibial band during heel strike | Assists in stabilizing the hip and knee via the iliotibial band during mid-stance | Assists in hip external rotation during heel-off and knee via the iliotibial band from mid-stance to heel and toe-off |

| | |
|---|---|
| *ORIGIN* | Iliac crest, sacrum, coccyx, sacrotuberous lig, sacroiliac ligament to aponeurosis to erector spinae |
| *INSERTION* | Iliotibial tract and posterior femur |
| *BY THE BOOK* | Hip extension and external rotation |

## HIP FLEXORS AND SUPRAILIAC: PSOAS, ILIACUS, QUADRATUS LUMBORUM

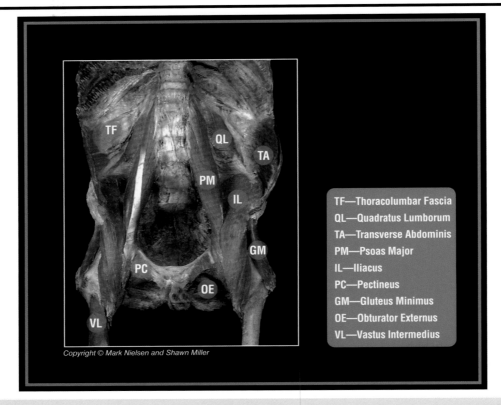

TF—Thoracolumbar Fascia
QL—Quadratus Lumborum
TA—Transverse Abdominis
PM—Psoas Major
IL—Iliacus
PC—Pectineus
GM—Gluteus Minimus
OE—Obturator Externus
VL—Vastus Intermedius

Copyright © Mark Nielsen and Shawn Miller

**PHOTO 3.11 HIP FLEXORS AND SUPRAILIAC: PSOAS, ILIACUS, AND QUADRATUS LUMBORUM**

Note: By way of the connection to the entire lumbar spine, the psoas assists in the dynamic stabilization of the lumbar spine during functional integrated activities. Psoas and iliacus share the same actions and are commonly referred as the iliopsoas, but are actually two separate and distinct tissues.

| FUNCTIONAL ACTION | PHASE 1: DECELERATION | PHASE 2: TRANSITION | PHASE 3: ACCELERATION |
|---|---|---|---|
| *SAGITTAL PLANE* | Assists with hip flexion during the swing phase prior to heel strike, and lumbo-pelvic-hip complex stabilization | Assists in lumbo-pelvic-hip complex stabilization | Assists in lumbo-pelvic-hip complex stabilization, assists with deceleration of hip extension through heel-off and toe-off |
| *FRONTAL PLANE* | Assists in deceleration of hip abduction of the same-side hip by way of fascial connection to the adductor group | Assists in lumbo-pelvic-hip complex stabilization | Assists in acceleration of hip adduction by way of fascial connection to the adductor group |
| *TRANSVERSE PLANE* | Assists with deceleration of hip (femoral) internal rotation during heel strike | Assists in lumbo-pelvic-hip complex stabilization | Assists with deceleration of hip (femoral) external rotation during heel-off |

| | |
|---|---|
| **ORIGIN OF PSOAS** | Transverse processes of lumbar vertebrae |
| **INSERTION** | Lesser trochanter of the femur |
| **BY THE BOOK** | Assists in concentric hip flexion, external rotation |
| **ORIGIN OF ILIACUS** | Iliac fossa |
| **INSERTION** | Lesser trochanter of the femur |
| **BY THE BOOK** | Assists in concentric hip flexion, external rotation |

## QUADRATUS LUMBORUM

| FUNCTIONAL ACTION | PHASE 1: DECELERATION | PHASE 2: TRANSITION | PHASE 3: ACCELERATION |
|---|---|---|---|
| **SAGITTAL PLANE** | Assists with deceleration of hip and lumbar flexion | Assists in lumbo-pelvic-hip complex stabilization during the swing phase | Assists in lumbo-pelvic-hip complex stabilization, assists with deceleration of hip extension through heel-off and toe-off |
| **FRONTAL PLANE** | Assists with deceleration of lateral flexion to the opposite side upon heel strike | Assists with lumbo-pelvic-hip complex stabilization along with the lateral gluteal complex during the swing phase | Assists with lumbo-pelvic-hip complex stabilization along with the lateral gluteal complex during heel-off |
| **TRANSVERSE PLANE** | Assists with deceleration of hip internal rotation to opposite side during heel strike and heel-off phases | Assists in lumbo-pelvic-hip complex stabilization during the swing phase | Assists with deceleration of hip (femoral) external rotation during heel-off and heel strike phases |

| | |
|---|---|
| **ORIGIN** | Iliac crest and iliolumbar ligament |
| **INSERTION** | Transverse process of L2-L5 vertebrae |
| **BY THE BOOK** | Concentric lateral flexion |

## ABDOMINAL COMPLEX

*Rectus Abdominis*
*External Obliques*
*Internal Obliques*
*Transverse Abdominis*

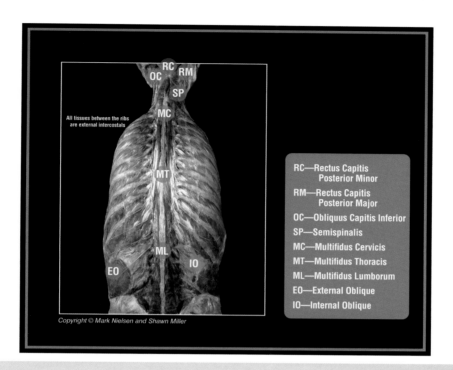

All tissues between the ribs
are external intercostals

RC—Rectus Capitis
　　　Posterior Minor
RM—Rectus Capitis
　　　Posterior Major
OC—Obliquus Capitis Inferior
SP—Semispinalis
MC—Multifidus Cervicis
MT—Multifidus Thoracis
ML—Multifidus Lumborum
EO—External Oblique
IO—Internal Oblique

Copyright © Mark Nielsen and Shawn Miller

**PHOTO 3.14 ERECTOR SPINAE, THE DEEP BACK MUSCLES**

## ILIOCOSTALIS, THORACIS, AND CERVICIS LUMBORUM

*(not shown as they lay superior to the muscles in these images)*

| FUNCTIONAL ACTION | PHASE 1: DECELERATION | PHASE 2: TRANSITION | PHASE 3: ACCELERATION |
|---|---|---|---|
| **SAGITTAL PLANE** | Assists in deceleration of spinal flexion | Assists in lumbar spine and pelvic stabilization | Assists in spinal extension |
| **FRONTAL PLANE** | Decelerates lateral flexion to the opposite side | Assists in lumbar spine and pelvic stabilization | Assists concentric lateral flexion to the same side |
| **TRANSVERSE PLANE** | Assists with deceleration of rotation of the spine and hips | Assists in lumbar spine and pelvic stabilization | Assists with acceleration of rotation of the spine |

| | |
|---|---|
| **ORIGIN** | Lumborum—upper lumbar and sacrum; Thoracis—upper border of the lower six ribs<br>Cervicis—superior border of ribs three through six medial to iliocostalis thoracis |
| **INSERTION** | Lumborum—tip of the transverse process of L1-4, ribs six through twelve<br>Thoracis—upper border of the upper six ribs to C7<br>Cervicis—posterior tubercles of the transverse process of C4-6 |
| **BY THE BOOK** | Spinal extension, lateral flexion, rotation |

## MULTIFIDUS LUMBORUM

| FUNCTIONAL ACTION | PHASE 1: DECELERATION | PHASE 2: TRANSITION | PHASE 3: ACCELERATION |
|---|---|---|---|
| *SAGITTAL PLANE* | Assists with deceleration of spinal flexion | Assists with lumbar spine and pelvic stabilization | Assists with spinal extension |
| *FRONTAL PLANE* | Decelerates lateral flexion to the opposite side in all phases of the gait cycle | Assists with lumbar spine and pelvic stabilization | Assists concentric lateral flexion to the same side in all phases of the gait cycle |
| *TRANSVERSE PLANE* | Assists with deceleration of rotation of the spine and hips in all phases of the gait cycle | Assists with lumbar spine and pelvic stabilization | Assists with acceleration of rotation of the spine |

| | |
|---|---|
| *ORIGIN* | Sacrum and lumbar transverse processes |
| *INSERTION* | Lumbar spinous process |
| *BY THE BOOK* | Spinal extension contralateral rotation |

## MULTIFIDUS CERVICIS

| FUNCTIONAL ACTION | PHASE 1: DECELERATION | PHASE 2: TRANSITION | PHASE 3: ACCELERATION |
|---|---|---|---|
| *SAGITTAL PLANE* | Assists in deceleration of cervical flexion | Stabilizes cervical spine | Assists in cervical extension |
| *FRONTAL PLANE* | Decelerates lateral flexion to the opposite side | Stabilizes cervical spine | Assists concentric lateral flexion to the same side |
| *TRANSVERSE PLANE* | Assists with deceleration of rotation of the cervical spine to the opposite side | Stabilizes cervical spine | Assists with acceleration of rotation of the cervical spine |

| | |
|---|---|
| *ORIGIN* | Cervical transverse process |
| *INSERTION* | Spinous process (may span two to four levels) |
| *BY THE BOOK* | Cervical extension and rotation |

# MULTIFIDUS THORACIS

| FUNCTIONAL ACTION | PHASE 1: DECELERATION | PHASE 2: TRANSITION | PHASE 3: ACCELERATION |
|---|---|---|---|
| *SAGITTAL PLANE* | Assists in deceleration of spinal flexion | Assists in spine stabilization | Assists in spine extension |
| *FRONTAL PLANE* | Decelerates lateral flexion to the opposite side | Assists in spine stabilization | Assists concentric lateral flexion to the same side |
| *TRANSVERSE PLANE* | Assists with deceleration of rotation of the spine | Assists in spine stabilization | Assists with acceleration of rotation of the spine |

| | |
|---|---|
| *ORIGIN* | Transverse processes of thoracic spine |
| *INSERTION* | Spinous process |
| *BY THE BOOK* | Spinal extension and rotation |

# LATISSIMUS DORSI AND TRAPEZIUS

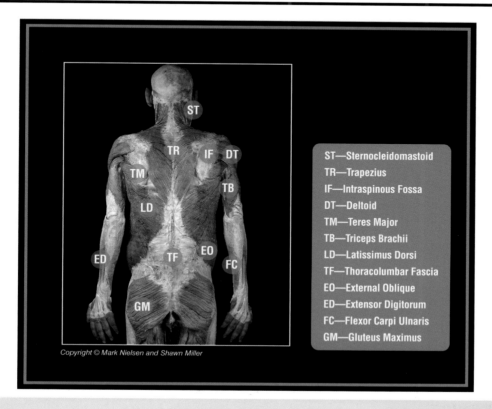

Copyright © Mark Nielsen and Shawn Miller

ST—Sternocleidomastoid
TR—Trapezius
IF—Intraspinous Fossa
DT—Deltoid
TM—Teres Major
TB—Triceps Brachii
LD—Latissimus Dorsi
TF—Thoracolumbar Fascia
EO—External Oblique
ED—Extensor Digitorum
FC—Flexor Carpi Ulnaris
GM—Gluteus Maximus

**PHOTO 3.15 LATISSIMUS DORSI AND TRAPEZIUS**

## LATISSIMUS DORSI

| FUNCTIONAL ACTION | PHASE 1: DECELERATION | PHASE 2: TRANSITION | PHASE 3: ACCELERATION |
|---|---|---|---|
| SAGITTAL PLANE | Assists in deceleration of shoulder flexion | Assists in lumbar spine and pelvic stabilization | Assists in shoulder extension |
| FRONTAL PLANE | Decelerates humeral abduction | Assists in lumbar spine and pelvic stabilization | Assists concentric arm adduction |
| TRANSVERSE PLANE | Assists in deceleration of external rotation of the arm | Assists with lumbar spine and pelvic stabilization | Assists with acceleration of internal rotation of the arm |

| | |
|---|---|
| ORIGIN | Posterior iliac crest, sacrum, thoracolumbar fascia, T7-L5 spinous process, ribs 9-12 |
| INSERTION | Intertubercular groove, fibers of external oblique between teres major and pec major |
| BY THE BOOK | Humeral adduction, external and internal rotation of humerus |

## TRAPEZIUS

| FUNCTIONAL ACTION | PHASE : DECELERATION | PHASE 2: TRANSITION | PHASE 3: ACCELERATION |
|---|---|---|---|
| SAGITTAL PLANE | Assists with deceleration upward rotation (lower and middle), decelerates cervical flexion (upper) | Assists with shoulder girdle and cervical spine stabilization | Assists with shoulder elevation (upper), cervical extension (upper) |
| FRONTAL PLANE | Assists with deceleration of scapular protraction | Assists with shoulder girdle and cervical spine stabilization | Assists concentric scapular retraction, depression |
| TRANSVERSE PLANE | Assists with deceleration of cervical rotation to the opposite side | Assists with shoulder girdle and cervical spine stabilization | Assists with acceleration of cervical rotation to the same side |

| | |
|---|---|
| ORIGIN | Occipital bone of the skull |
| INSERTION | Acromion, scapular spine, and lateral clavicle |
| BY THE BOOK | Assists in scapular elevation, retraction, and depression |

# UPPER BACK

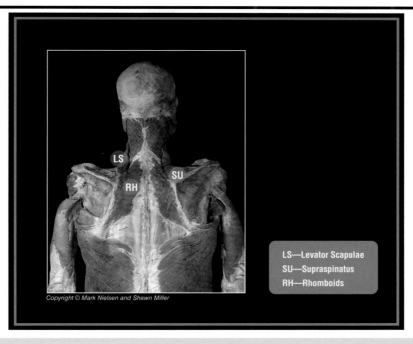

LS—Levator Scapulae
SU—Supraspinatus
RH—Rhomboids

Copyright © Mark Nielsen and Shawn Miller

PHOTO 3.16 RHOMBOIDS, SUPRASPINATUS (SEE SHOULDER COMPLEX), AND LEVATOR SCAPULAE

# RHOMBOIDS

| FUNCTIONAL ACTION | PHASE 1: DECELERATION | PHASE 2: TRANSITION | PHASE 3: ACCELERATION |
|---|---|---|---|
| *SAGITTAL PLANE* | Assists with deceleration upward rotation | Assists with shoulder stabilization | Assists with shoulder depression |
| *FRONTAL PLANE* | Assists with deceleration of scapular protraction | Assists with shoulder stabilization | Assists concentric scapular retraction |
| *TRANSVERSE PLANE* | Assists with deceleration of internal rotation of the shoulder girdle during actions requiring a reach across | Assists with shoulder girdle stabilization | Assists with acceleration of external rotation of the shoulder girdle |

| | |
|---|---|
| *ORIGIN* | Spinous processes C-7 through T-5 |
| *INSERTION* | Medial border of the scapula and medial 30% of anterior surface of the scapula |
| *BY THE BOOK* | Assists in scapular retraction and depression |

## LEVATOR SCAPULAE

| FUNCTIONAL ACTION | PHASE 1: DECELERATION | PHASE 2: TRANSITION | PHASE 3: ACCELERATION |
|---|---|---|---|
| *SAGITTAL PLANE* | Decelerates cervical flexion | Stabilizes C-spine and scapular complex | Assists with acceleration of cervical extension |
| *FRONTAL PLANE* | The tissue on one side synergistically assists in deceleration of cervical lateral flexion to the opposite side | Stabilizes C-spine and scapular complex | Synergistically assists in acceleration of cervical lateral flexion back to neutral |
| *TRANSVERSE PLANE* | Assists with deceleration of cervical rotation to the opposite side | Stabilizes C-spine and scapular complex | Assists with acceleration of cervical rotation back to same side |

| | |
|---|---|
| *ORIGIN* | Transverse process of C1-C4 |
| *INSERTION* | Superior medial border of the scapula |
| *BY THE BOOK* | Cervical extension, assists in scapular elevation and depression, lateral cervical flexion |

## SHOULDER COMPLEX

*Supraspinatus*
*Subscapularis*
*Infraspinatus*
*Teres Minor*
*Deltoid*
*Pectoralis Major and Minor*
*Serratus Anterior*

# SUPRASPINATUS

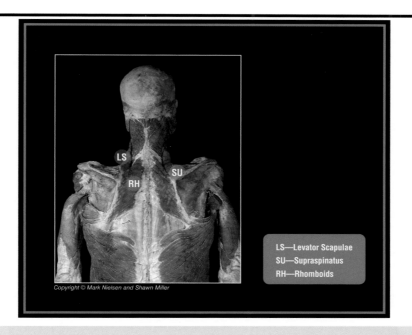

LS—Levator Scapulae
SU—Supraspinatus
RH—Rhomboids

Copyright © Mark Nielsen and Shawn Miller

PHOTO 3.17 SUPRASPINATUS

## SUPRASPINATUS

| FUNCTIONAL ACTION | PHASE 1: DECELERATION | PHASE 2: TRANSITION | PHASE 3: ACCELERATION |
|---|---|---|---|
| **SAGITTAL PLANE** | Stabilizes the humeral head during humeral motion | Synergistically assists in stabilization of the shoulder girdle with other rotator cuff muscles | Stabilizes the humeral head during humeral motion |
| **FRONTAL PLANE** | Synergistically assists in deceleration of humeral adduction and assists in providing an inferior glide during abduction and scapular elevation | Synergistically assists in stabilization of the shoulder girdle with other rotator cuff muscles | Synergistically assists in acceleration of humeral abduction |
| **TRANSVERSE PLANE** | Assists with deceleration of humeral internal and external rotation | Synergistically assists in stabilization of the shoulder girdle with other rotator cuff muscles | Assists with acceleration of humeral external and internal rotation |

| | |
|---|---|
| **ORIGIN** | Superior scapular fossa |
| **INSERTION** | Superior humeral tubercle |
| **BY THE BOOK** | Humeral abduction |

## SUBSCAPULARIS

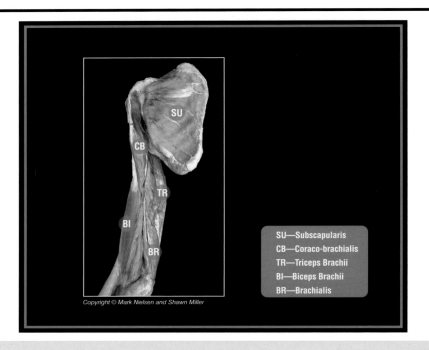

SU—Subscapularis
CB—Coraco-brachialis
TR—Triceps Brachii
BI—Biceps Brachii
BR—Brachialis

Copyright © Mark Nielsen and Shawn Miller

**PHOTO 3.18 SUBSCAPULARIS**

## SUBSCAPULARIS

| FUNCTIONAL ACTION | PHASE 1: DECELERATION | PHASE 2: TRANSITION | PHASE 3: ACCELERATION |
|---|---|---|---|
| **SAGITTAL PLANE** | Stabilizes the humeral head during humeral extension | Synergistically assists in stabilization of the shoulder girdle with other rotator cuff muscles | Stabilizes the humeral head during humeral flexion motion |
| **FRONTAL PLANE** | Synergistically assists in deceleration of humeral abduction | Synergistically assists in stabilization of the shoulder girdle with other rotator cuff muscles | Synergistically assists in acceleration of humeral adduction |
| **TRANSVERSE PLANE** | Assists with deceleration of humeral external rotation | Synergistically assists in stabilization of the shoulder girdle with other rotator cuff muscles | Assists with acceleration of humeral internal rotation |

| | |
|---|---|
| **ORIGIN** | Scapular fossa |
| **INSERTION** | Lesser humeral tubercle |
| **BY THE BOOK** | Internal rotation of humerus |

# INFRASPINATUS AND TERES MINOR

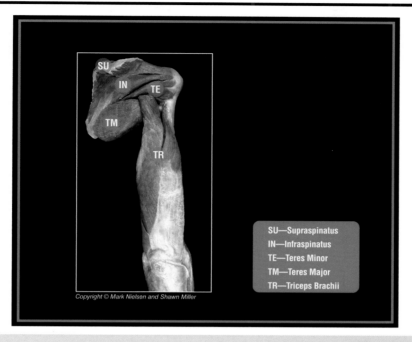

SU—Supraspinatus
IN—Infraspinatus
TE—Teres Minor
TM—Teres Major
TR—Triceps Brachii

Copyright © Mark Nielsen and Shawn Miller

PHOTO 3.19 INFRASPINATUS AND TERES MINOR

# INFRASPINATUS

| FUNCTIONAL ACTION | PHASE 1: DECELERATION | PHASE 2: TRANSITION | PHASE 3: ACCELERATION |
|---|---|---|---|
| **SAGITTAL PLANE** | Stabilizes the humeral head during shoulder flexion | Synergistically assists in stabilization of the shoulder girdle with other rotator cuff muscles | Stabilizes the humeral head during shoulder extension |
| **FRONTAL PLANE** | Synergistically assists in deceleration of humeral abduction and assists in providing an inferior glide during abduction and scapular elevation | Synergistically assists in stabilization of the shoulder girdle with other rotator cuff muscles | Synergistically assists in acceleration of humeral adduction |
| **TRANSVERSE PLANE** | Assists with deceleration of humeral internal rotation | Synergistically assists in stabilization of the shoulder girdle with other rotator cuff muscles | Assists with acceleration of humeral external rotation |

| | |
|---|---|
| **ORIGIN** | Infraspinatus scapular fossa |
| **INSERTION** | Posterior humeral greater tuberosity |
| **BY THE BOOK** | Humeral external rotation |

# TERES MINOR

| FUNCTIONAL ACTION | PHASE 1: DECELERATION | PHASE 2: TRANSITION | PHASE 3: ACCELERATION |
|---|---|---|---|
| **SAGITTAL PLANE** | Stabilizes the humeral head during shoulder flexion | Synergistically assists in stabilization of the shoulder girdle with other rotator cuff muscles | Stabilizes the humeral head during shoulder extension |
| **FRONTAL PLANE** | Synergistically assists in deceleration of humeral abduction and assists in providing an inferior glide during abduction and scapular elevation | Synergistically assists in stabilization of the shoulder girdle with other rotator cuff muscles | Synergistically assists in acceleration of humeral adduction |
| **TRANSVERSE PLANE** | Assists with deceleration of humeral internal rotation | Synergistically assists in stabilization of the shoulder girdle with other rotator cuff muscles | Assists with acceleration of humeral external rotation |

| | |
|---|---|
| **ORIGIN** | Lateral scapula on the posterior side |
| **INSERTION** | Posterior humeral greater tuberosity shared with infraspinatus insertion |
| **BY THE BOOK** | Humeral external rotation |

## DELTOID

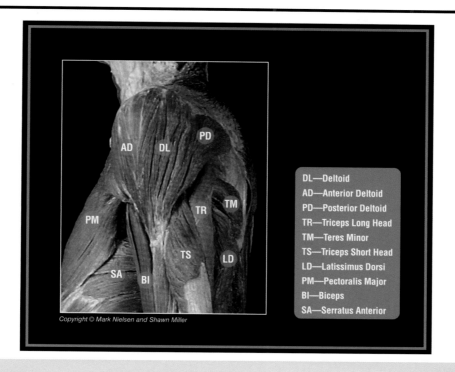

DL—Deltoid
AD—Anterior Deltoid
PD—Posterior Deltoid
TR—Triceps Long Head
TM—Teres Minor
TS—Triceps Short Head
LD—Latissimus Dorsi
PM—Pectoralis Major
BI—Biceps
SA—Serratus Anterior

Copyright © Mark Nielsen and Shawn Miller

**PHOTO 3.20 DELTOID**

| FUNCTIONAL ACTION | PHASE 1: DECELERATION | PHASE 2: TRANSITION | PHASE 3: ACCELERATION |
|---|---|---|---|
| **SAGITTAL PLANE** | Assists with deceleration of shoulder extension (anterior); assists with deceleration of shoulder flexion (posterior) | Synergistically assists in stabilization of the shoulder girdle with other rotator cuff muscles | Assists with acceleration of shoulder flexion (anterior); Assists with acceleration of shoulder extension (posterior) |
| **FRONTAL PLANE** | Assists with deceleration of shoulder adduction | Synergistically assists in stabilization of the shoulder girdle with other rotator cuff muscles | Assists with acceleration of shoulder abduction |
| **TRANSVERSE PLANE** | Assists with deceleration of humeral external rotation (anterior); internal rotation (posterior) | Synergistically assists in stabilization of the shoulder girdle with other rotator cuff muscles | Assists with acceleration of humeral internal rotation |

| | |
|---|---|
| **ORIGIN** | Spine and acromion of scapula and lateral clavicle |
| **INSERTION** | Deltoid tuberosity of humerus and brachial fossa |
| **BY THE BOOK** | Flexion, abduction, extension, internal rotation, and external rotation of shoulder |

## PECTORAL MAJOR AND MINOR

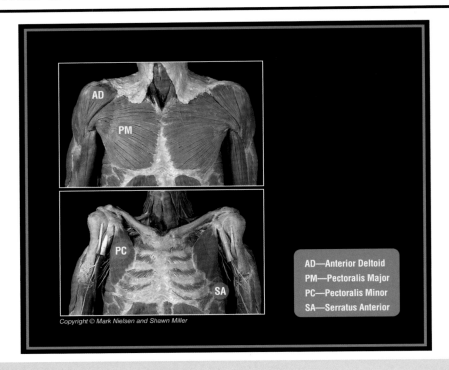

AD—Anterior Deltoid
PM—Pectoralis Major
PC—Pectoralis Minor
SA—Serratus Anterior

Copyright © Mark Nielsen and Shawn Miller

PHOTO 3.21 PECTORALS

## PECTORAL MAJOR AND MINOR

| FUNCTIONAL ACTION | PHASE 1: DECELERATION | PHASE 2: TRANSITION | PHASE 3: ACCELERATION |
|---|---|---|---|
| **SAGITTAL PLANE** | Assists with deceleration of shoulder extension | Assists with shoulder stabilization, especially in overhead movements | Assists with shoulder flexion |
| **FRONTAL PLANE** | Assists with deceleration of shoulder abduction | Assists with shoulder stabilization, especially in overhead movements | Assists with concentric shoulder adduction |
| **TRANSVERSE PLANE** | Assists with deceleration of external rotation of the arm | Assists with shoulder stabilization, especially in overhead movements | Assists with acceleration of internal rotation of the arm |

| | |
|---|---|
| **ORIGIN** | Clavicle, sternum, ribs one through seven, aponeurosis of the external oblique |
| **INSERTION** | Greater tubercle of the humerus |
| **BY THE BOOK** | Shoulder flexion, adduction, internal rotation |

## SERRATUS ANTERIOR

| FUNCTIONAL ACTION | PHASE 1: DECELERATION | PHASE 2: TRANSITION | PHASE 3: ACCELERATION |
|---|---|---|---|
| *SAGITTAL PLANE* | Assists with deceleration of scapular retraction | Assists with the trapezius to provide scapular mobility and stability during shoulder girdle elevation | Assists with shoulder girdle dynamic stability |
| *FRONTAL PLANE* | Assists with deceleration of scapular retraction | Assists with the trapezius to provide scapular mobility and stability during shoulder girdle elevation | Assists with shoulder girdle dynamic stability |
| *TRANSVERSE PLANE* | Assists with deceleration of scapular retraction | Assists with the trapezius to provide scapular mobility and stability during shoulder girdle elevation | Assists with shoulder girdle dynamic stability |

| | |
|---|---|
| *ORIGIN* | Anterolateral surface of the first eight or nine ribs just anterior to the mid-axillary line |
| *INSERTION* | Anterior surface of the medial border of the scapula |
| *BY THE BOOK* | Scapular protraction |

**About the serratus anterior:** *Many shoulder impingement issues are related to the tightness of the serratus anterior. This tissue must have the mobility to allow the scapula to glide over the ribs, especially with scapular protraction and retraction movements. If this muscle is tight, the scapulohumeral rhythms are negatively affected and can increase the risk of the supraspinatus tendon becoming impinged between the acromion process and the humeral head.*

*Scapular winging is often related to as a weak serratus anterior.*

## UPPER EXTREMITY

*Triceps*
*Biceps Brachii*
*Brachialis*
*Brachioradialis*

# TRICEPS

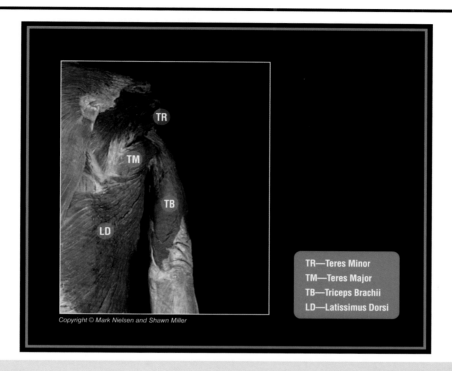

TR—Teres Minor
TM—Teres Major
TB—Triceps Brachii
LD—Latissimus Dorsi

Copyright © Mark Nielsen and Shawn Miller

**PHOTO 3.22 TRICEPS**

| FUNCTIONAL ACTION | PHASE 1: DECELERATION | PHASE 2: TRANSITION | PHASE 3: ACCELERATION |
|---|---|---|---|
| *SAGITTAL PLANE* | Assists with deceleration of the elbow and shoulder flexion | Synergistically assists in stabilization of the shoulder joint and elbow | Assists with acceleration of the elbow and shoulder extension |
| *FRONTAL PLANE* | Synergistically assists in stabilization of the shoulder girdle | Synergistically assists in stabilization of the shoulder girdle | Synergistically assists in stabilization of the shoulder girdle |
| *TRANSVERSE PLANE* | Assists with deceleration of humeral internal rotation | Synergistically assists in stabilization of the shoulder girdle with other rotator cuff muscles | Assists with acceleration of humeral external rotation |

| | |
|---|---|
| *ORIGIN* | Long head—infraglenoid tubercle of scapula<br>Medial and lateral heads—posterior humerus |
| *INSERTION* | Tendon to olecranon process of ulna |
| *BY THE BOOK* | Elbow and shoulder extension |

## BICEPS GROUP

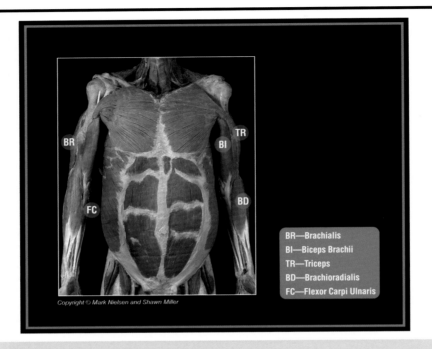

BR—Brachialis
BI—Biceps Brachii
TR—Triceps
BD—Brachioradialis
FC—Flexor Carpi Ulnaris

Copyright © Mark Nielsen and Shawn Miller

PHOTO 3.23 BICEPS GROUP

## BICEPS BRACHII

| FUNCTIONAL ACTION | PHASE 1: DECELERATION | PHASE 2: TRANSITION | PHASE 3: ACCELERATION |
|---|---|---|---|
| **SAGITTAL PLANE** | Assists with deceleration of elbow extension and shoulder extension | Assists with stabilization of the shoulder complex | Assists with elbow flexion and shoulder flexion |
| **FRONTAL PLANE** | Assists with deceleration of horizontal shoulder abduction; and shoulder and elbow flexion when the shoulder is abducted. Note that these actions take place in the transverse plane | Assists with stabilization of the shoulder complex | Assists with horizontal shoulder adduction; and shoulder and elbow flexion when the shoulder is abducted. Note that these actions take place in the transverse plane |
| **TRANSVERSE PLANE** | Assists with deceleration of radioulnar pronation | Assists with stabilization of the shoulder complex | Assists with acceleration of radioulnar acceleration and humeral functional movements |

| | |
|---|---|
| **ORIGIN** | Short head—coracoid process<br>Long head—tubercle above glenoid cavity and rim of glenoid |
| **INSERTION** | Radial tuberosity |
| **BY THE BOOK** | Assists elbow flexion, supination of radioulnar joint, and shoulder flexion |

## BRACHIALIS

| FUNCTIONAL ACTION | PHASE 1: DECELERATION | PHASE 2: TRANSITION | PHASE 3: ACCELERATION |
| --- | --- | --- | --- |
| **SAGITTAL PLANE** | Assists with deceleration of the elbow extension | Synergistically assists in elbow stabilization | Assists in elbow flexion |
| **FRONTAL PLANE** | Elbow stability | Synergistically assists in elbow stabilization | Elbow stability |
| **TRANSVERSE PLANE** | Assists with deceleration of forearm pronation | Synergistically assists in elbow stabilization | Assists with acceleration of forearm supination |

| | |
| --- | --- |
| **ORIGIN** | Anterior distal half of humerus |
| **INSERTION** | Coronoid process of ulna and capsule of elbow joint |
| **BY THE BOOK** | Elbow flexion |

## BRACHIORADIALIS

| FUNCTIONAL ACTION | PHASE 1: DECELERATION | PHASE 2: TRANSITION | PHASE 3: ACCELERATION |
| --- | --- | --- | --- |
| **SAGITTAL PLANE** | Assists with deceleration of elbow extension | Synergistically assists with elbow stabilization | Assists with acceleration of elbow flexion |
| **FRONTAL PLANE** | Elbow stability | Synergistically assists with elbow stabilization | Elbow stability |
| **TRANSVERSE PLANE** | Assists with deceleration of forearm pronation | Synergistically assists in elbow stabilization | Assists with acceleration of forearm supination |

| | |
| --- | --- |
| **ORIGIN** | Supracondylar ridge of humerus |
| **INSERTION** | Styloid of radius |
| **BY THE BOOK** | Elbow flexion, synergistic with biceps and brachialis |

## ANATOMY IN FUNCTION

Anatomical anatomy teaches the actions of each muscle in an isolated manner. As important as this information is, it will make your understanding of movement easier if you think in terms of regional tissue categories.

For example, the calf has the connotation of the gastrocnemius and soleus, and according to the anatomy and kinesiology books, both work synergistically to cause plantar flexion. In isolation this is true; however, when analyzing ankle function and looking at the muscle function chart on page 37, we see there are actually seven muscles in this region.

The rationale for regions is based on the fascial webbing that unifies these tissues to produce a tri-phasic, tri-plane reaction of the tissues that synergistically results in a specific action.

The muscle tissue of the calf also affects the foot. When the foot and ankle complex is loaded, there are four mechanisms required for successful motion: calcaneal eversion, ankle dorsiflexion, tibial internal rotation, and forefoot abduction. As the calcaneus forms a fulcrum with the ground at heel strike, the foot falls to the ground while moving through relative ankle plantar flexion.

In *function,* the calf does not cause the ankle to plantarflex as the foot goes to the ground. Gravity brings the foot forward. However, this reaction is controlled as the anterior tibialis and extensor digitorum eccentrically load with deceleration of ankle plantar flexion. Neither of these tissues do this in isolation; rather, they do it synergistically.

With the foot firmly on the ground, the tibia moves over the foot, resulting in ankle dorsiflexion; the calcaneus everts, the midtarsals unlock and the forefoot abducts in relation to the rearfoot. Concurrently, the tibia will internally rotate.

To control and decelerate these actions, the gastrocnemius loads to slow the tibia's movement over the foot in the sagittal plane. Additionally, the soleus does the same, as does the tibialis posterior. In the frontal plane, the tibialis posterior decelerates calcaneal eversion, and also slows the navicular into eversion. As these bones move in the frontal plane, the tibia then rotates inward.

The accumulative reactions of the gastrocnemius, soleus, and posterior tibialis assist with deceleration of tibial internal rotation. These tissues work synergistically and in three planes of motion.

Study the images and tables in this chapter. Then get up and move to feel how these myofascial tissues create an environment for successful movement.

These actions are vastly different than the actions described in anatomical anatomy books. We need to comprehend both types of anatomy—anatomical and functional.

# CHAPTER FOUR

# WORKING AROUND THE JOINTS

*"The proper function of man is to live, not to exist."*

~ J A C K   L O N D O N

Efficient body movements are a series of reactions to produce a desired outcome. Similar to an intricate pattern of dominoes, a piece must fall forward or have an external influence to move that causes the falling of adjacent pieces, creating a mechanical chain reaction.

The body is no different, requiring an external force to initiate a series of cascading reactions to produce a desired outcome. The most common of events, such as walking or running, start with a change of body angle that impacts the center of mass and the body falls forward. Subconsciously, the nervous system reacts and places the foot in a position to prevent the body from falling, so it can then react to create a desired outcome of walking or running.

With this premise in mind, we will begin with the foot movements and their impact on the series of synergistic reactions that occur within the body when in upright positions.

## THE FOOT

To appreciate integrated human movement, we need to take the time to understand the tremendous impact the foot has on our entire movement system. When you internalize this, it will change the way you watch others move and will also have great implications on your corrective strategies for your clients.

The foot is a mobile adapter and is one of the most fascinating and complex structures in the body. Being a mobile adapter means the foot attempts to stay level by trying to keep the first and fifth metatarsal joints and the calcaneus level with the ground beneath it. Comprised of 24 muscles, 26 bones, and 33 joints, the foot is the conduit that interfaces with the ground and sets the platform on which the body reacts.

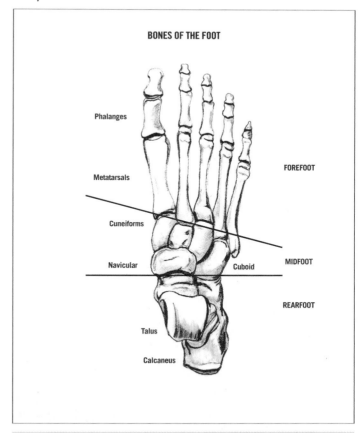

BONES OF THE FOOT

Phalanges

FOREFOOT

Metatarsals

Cuneiforms

MIDFOOT

Navicular — Cuboid

REARFOOT

Talus

Calcaneus

**FIGURE 4.1 BONES OF THE FOOT**

According to Rene Cailliet, MD, in his book *Foot and Ankle Pain, Edition 3,* the foot is categorized into three regions: the forefoot, midfoot, and rearfoot. The forefoot consists of the toes (phalanges) and the long bones (metatarsals). Each of the phalanges from toes two to five has three bones and two joints, while the great toe has two bones and one joint.

The midfoot includes the three cuneiforms (medial, intermediate, and lateral), the navicular on the medial column, and the cuboid on the lateral column. These five bones form the midfoot arch and must be mobile enough to absorb forces during the "collapsing" of the arch through pronation.

The calcaneus and talus make up the rearfoot. The calcaneus has a concave surface on the superior aspect and the talus is convex at the inferior surface. The union of the calcaneus and talus form the subtalar joint, an extremely important joint that sets the environment for successful tri-plane motion.

To think through the action of the rearfoot, let's use the analogy of a bicyclist riding a bike. Imagine the cyclist riding along and then starts to lose balance. The bike falls to the right, while the bottom of the tires turn outward to the left. See Photo 4.1.

**PHOTO 4.1 CYCLIST TILTING RIGHT**

In our analogy, the bike and tires are the calcaneus, while the rider is the talus wearing a long helmet called the tibia—the tibia sits atop the talus.

As the bike "falls" to the right, the bottom of the tires turn outward toward the left, similar to the left foot hitting the ground and causing the calcaneus to evert—the heel "falls" right, while the bottom of the heel turns outward to the left.

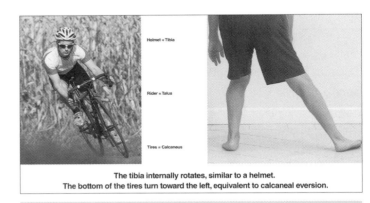

The tibia internally rotates, similar to a helmet.
The bottom of the tires turn toward the left, equivalent to calcaneal eversion.

**PHOTO 4.2 VIEWING A CYCLIST AS THE ANKLE COMPLEX**

With the foot on the ground during the landing phase of gait, the medial column of the foot, composed of the union of the talus and navicular forming the talo-navicular joint, falls medially toward the ground.

Based on the axis of motion, the talo-navicular and subtalar joints' primary motions are eversion and inversion in the frontal plane. This motion allows the tibia to move farther forward in the sagittal plane and to dorsiflex at the ankle, while also internally rotating in the transverse plane.

Most texts discuss the sagittal plane of the ankle, and in the isolated sense, the talocrural joint—the ankle—is strictly a sagittal-plane mover. However, as the foot loads when hitting the ground, the ankle dorsiflexes in the sagittal plane, the calcaneus everts causing the subtalar joint to evert in the frontal plane, and the tibia internally rotates in the transverse plane.

This reaction then causes the midfoot to evert in the frontal plane. The forefoot abducts in relation to the mid and rearfoot—remember the concept of motion as the distal bone in relation to the proximal bone segments.

Because the rearfoot and midfoot move farther and faster than the forefoot in the frontal plane, the metatarsals and phalanges are lateral to the proximal segments, and are therefore abducted to the rearfoot.

These motions show that the foot and ankle complex is moving in three planes of motion.

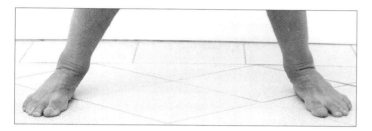

**PHOTO 4.3 EVERSION AND ABDUCTION**

*The rearfoot and midfoot move farther and faster than the forefoot in the frontal plane; the metatarsals and phalanges are lateral to the proximal segments of the talus and calcaneus in the rearfoot and are therefore abducted to the rearfoot.*

We want mobility in the foot during the pronation phase to allow the absorption of forces. Yet, as ambulation takes place and the hip moves over the foot, the opposing swing leg drives the opposing hip forward, which inverts the calcaneus, plantar flexes the ankle, externally rotates the tibia, and adducts the forefoot of the stance leg.

**PHOTOS 4.4 A, B, C THE GAIT SEQUENCE FROM THE FRONT**

**PHOTOS 4.5 A, B, C THE GAIT SEQUENCE FROM THE REAR**

**PHOTOS 4.6 A, B, C THE GAIT SEQUENCE FROM THE SIDE**

*In the photo sequence, notice the left leg and foot. The leg is externally rotated and the foot is inverted. As the foot hits the ground, the foot pronates, which enhances relative dorsiflexion, tibial internal rotation, and forefoot abduction. As the hip moves over the foot, the rear heel rises off the ground, the foot inverts and "locks up" the midfoot, enabling the foot to be a cantilever to propel ankle plantar flexion, extension of the metatarsals, forefoot adduction, tibial external rotation, and hip extension.*

In motion, the ankle joint moves primarily in the sagittal plane. It needs some degree of frontal-plane action, but not to the point that it creates too much mobility, which increases the risk of ankle injuries. This concept is very important, as it is critical for the foot and ankle to undergo these actions to create an environment for successful knee and hip function.

As a review, when the foot hits the ground in the prona-tion phase, the lower extremity is eccentrically loaded by virtue of:

- *Calcaneal eversion*
- *Ankle dorsiflexion*
- *Tibial internal rotation*
- *Forefoot abduction*

## THE KNEE

Books describe knee motion primarily in the sagittal plane as it flexes and extends. Health and sports performance professionals frequently preach that the knee must be stable in side-to-side or frontal-plane motion. Rarely, however, do we hear that the knee must move in the frontal and trans-verse planes when the knee flexes to decelerate movement.

Numerous articles have been written stating the knee must track over the second and third metatarsals when doing a lunge or a squat. If this is the case, why does nearly every athletic movement requiring deceleration and change of direction to the medial side of the knee cause the knee to move medially to the foot and hip as shown in Photo 4.7?

**PHOTO 4.7 LEFT KNEE MEDIAL TO THE LEFT FOOT**

*Notice how the hitter's left knee is medial to the left foot. This allows the hip to eccentrically load as the player drives off the left foot in preparation to run.*

As the foot moves through pronation via calcaneal eversion, dorsiflexion, tibial internal rotation, and fore-foot abduction, the tibia internally rotates on the talus.

To feel this for yourself, stand up and perform a lunge, placing your hand on the tibial line of the lung-ing leg as you move. In a successful lunge, you should notice the calcaneus everting, the ankle dorsiflexing, and the tibia turning inward as the knee flexes. The tibia is internally rotated to the femur and therefore the distal bone (tibia) in relation to the proximal bone (femur) will place the knee into internal rotation in the transverse plane.

Likewise, if we view the distal end of the tibia in rela-tion to the distal end of the femur, the tibia is lateral to the femur, and therefore is described as being abducted in the frontal plane. This can be confusing because people see the knee joint move toward the midline and think the knee is adducted. But using the principles of movement, the distal bone is abducted to the proximal bone, thereby positioning the knee in knee abduction.

I call the knee "the dumbest joint in the body," because it is highly influenced by foot motion and posi-tion, as well as by that of the hip. Consequently, we do not need to be overly concerned when the knee moves medially to the foot. However, we should be very con-cerned with *why* the knee moves and reacts the way it does.

If a client does a lunge or a squat and cannot return to the starting position with a smooth transition, we should have major concerns why that may be the case. We must look at foot function as well as hip function to help the knee be successful.

To review, the knee should be fairly mobile in the sagittal plane, but also must have some degree of trans-verse-plane and frontal-plane mobility. We raise a cau-tionary eye to how smooth, efficient, and successful the transition is from loading the knee, and how much con-trol is demonstrated when moving through the frontal plane and returning to the starting position.

If the movement looks uncontrolled and sloppy, we should prescribe strengthening and corrective exercises to stabilize that action. But never should there be such stability at the knee that no frontal or transverse-plane motion can occur.

The actions that promote successful knee function are:

- *Knee flexion in the sagittal plane*
- *Knee abduction in the frontal plane via the tibia being abducted (lateral) to the femur*
- *Knee internal rotation as a result of tibial internal rotation in relation to the femur*

## THE HIP

The hip complex is one of the most mobile regions of the body. A myriad of dysfunctions can develop when the hip is immobile in one or more planes of motion. On that list would be knee pain, sacroiliac pain, low back pain, and even shoulder discomfort.

We start our study from the foot reaction as the foot pronates, the calcaneus everts, the ankle dorsiflexes, the tibia internally rotates, and the forefoot abducts. When the hip loads in three planes of motion, such as in a squat, the tibia internally rotates and the knee flexes in the sagittal plane, abducts in the frontal plane, and internally rotates in the transverse plane.

As the femur reacts to the other motions below it, the forward motion of the femur reduces the angle between the femur and ilium and results in hip flexion in the sagittal plane.

Simultaneously, as the knee abducts, the femur is "pulled" medially, causing hip adduction because the distal bone (femur) is now medial to the proximal bone (ilium). The alignment of the femur in relation to the ilium and knee causes the femur to internally rotate in relation to the ilium when loading the hip.

Study Figure 4.2 to envision the tri-plane actions of the hip and knee.

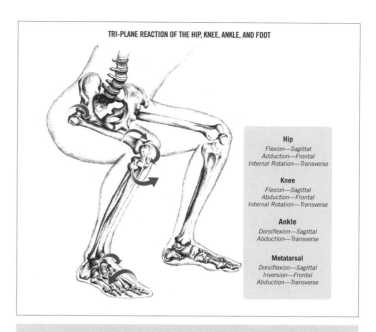

TRI-PLANE REACTION OF THE HIP, KNEE, ANKLE, AND FOOT

**Hip**
*Flexion—Sagittal*
*Adduction—Frontal*
*Internal Rotation—Transverse*

**Knee**
*Flexion—Sagittal*
*Abduction—Frontal*
*Internal Rotation—Transverse*

**Ankle**
*Dorsiflexion—Sagittal*
*Abduction—Transverse*

**Metatarsal**
*Dorsiflexion—Sagittal*
*Inversion—Frontal*
*Abduction—Transverse*

**FIGURE 4.2 TRI-PLANE ACTIONS OF THE HIP, KNEE, ANKLE, AND FOOT**

The gluteal complex, especially the gluteus maximus, is attached at the greater trochanter, the gluteal line, and the posterior superior iliac spine. The gluteal tissue is eccentrically loaded as the hip flexes, adducts, and internally rotates.

In Photo 4.8, notice the relationship of the bone segments that load the hip in all three planes of motion during this frontal-plane lunge with opposite lateral reach.

**PHOTO 4.8 FRONTAL-PLANE LUNGE WITH OPPOSITE LATERAL ARM REACH**

**PHOTO 4.9 LEFT LEG FORWARD IN GAIT WITH OPPOSITE ARM REACH**

During the gait cycle, all of the above actions occur on the weight-bearing side as a person ambulates forward. Bring your attention to the motion of the non-weight–bearing side as the leg swings through to the next step. For consistency, consider the left side as the right leg is about to swing through during the gait cycle.

Referring to Photo 4.9, just prior to the right heel lifting off the ground, the pelvis is rotated to the right. As the heel lifts off the ground, the pelvis starts to rotate left, creating an externally rotated right hip as the ilium rotates farther left than the femur. The femur is rotated right—it is externally rotated—to the ilium in the transverse plane.

As the right leg begins to swing forward, the right hip is lower than the left and slightly medial to the right leg. Since the right leg is lateral to the ilium, the right hip is abducted during this swing phase.

Additionally, the right leg is extended from the hip; hence, the hip is extended in the sagittal plane. All these actions are critical for shock absorption, force production, and force transmission during an efficient gait cycle. This is vital for reducing overuse issues, especially in commonly injured areas such as the lumbar spine.

During the swing phase of gait, the right leg will swing through. At some point prior to heel-off, the right hip will reach its maximal extension and the ankle will attain maximal dorsiflexion. The tissue of the calf group will be fully eccentrically loaded and the tissue of the foot will become taut. This causes the bones of the foot to become close packed or "locked up" and is concomitant as the body continues to move forward.

This reaction will elicit heel-off, while it will simultaneously invert the calcaneus, adduct the forefoot, externally rotate the tibia, and externally rotate the femur. With the foot in a supinated position, this allows a cantilever effect as the metatarsals move through dorsiflexion to propel the body forward.

As the weight transfer moves toward the left hip, the right ilium becomes medial to the right femur, resulting in right hip abduction. As these reactions progress and the body mass moves toward the left side, the left foot will move through calcaneal eversion, ankle dorsiflexion, tibial internal rotation, and forefoot abduction. This causes the same reactions as the right femur and hip as discussed earlier.

As the right leg swings through, it will carry the right hip and pelvic girdle. As the pelvis swings to the left and with the left foot fixed on the ground, the left ilium internally rotates on the femur, resulting in left-hip internal rotation.

As a review, for successful movement, the weight-bearing hip moves in three planes of motion and undergoes loading or deceleration during the following actions:

- *Hip flexion in the sagittal plane*
- *Hip adduction in the frontal plane*
- *Hip internal rotation in the transverse plane*

With the extended, non-weight–bearing hip at heel-off, look for:

- *Hip extension in the sagittal plane*
- *Hip abduction in the frontal plane*
- *Hip external rotation in the transverse plane*

## THE LUMBAR SPINE

The lumbar spine is the nemesis of fitness and health professionals. Arguably, low-back problems account for the majority of missed workdays and industrial injuries. Approximately 80% of adults will suffer from muscular low-back pain at some point in their lives. Low-back pain accounts for more than $90 billion in costs in the United States, and greater than $216 billion

globally. This alone makes lumbar spine issues worth our attention.

Prior to embarking on a description of lumbar spine movements, we need to consider a foundational concept relating to movement of the back:

*Movements of the joints of the extremities are described as the distal bone moving in relation to the proximal bone. However, in the spine it is the opposite. Spinal motion is described as the proximal bone in relation to the distal bone.*

Referring to Photos 4.10 and 4.11, the first picture shows left cervical rotation because the proximal segment is rotated farther to the left than the segments below it. In Photo 4.10, the head is turned left and the body is straight ahead. The relative positions of the head and cervical spine to the rest of the body are left rotation, with the key term here as "relative rotation."

However, Photo 4.11 also demonstrates left cervical rotation because the proximal cervical segments are rotated farther left than the distal vertebra below. The position shows the body as rotated right, while the head is straight ahead. Once again, the key term is "relative rotation." Using this foundational concept, this translates to left cervical rotation.

**PHOTO 4.10 C-SPINE ROTATION TO THE LEFT, THE HEAD IS ROTATED TO THE LEFT WHILE THE BODY IS STRAIGHT FORWARD. THIS IS RELATIVE ROTATION OF PROXIMAL BONE SEGMENTS TO THE DISTAL BONE SEGMENTS.**

**PHOTO 4.11 C-SPINE ROTATION TO THE LEFT, THE BODY IS ROTATED TO THE RIGHT WHILE THE HEAD IS FORWARD. THIS IS RELATIVE ROTATION OF PROXIMAL BONE SEGMENTS TO THE DISTAL BONE SEGMENTS.**

The entire spine can be difficult to visualize three-dimensionally, but with careful and deliberate thought, you will learn how to do it. This will help you assist your clients into a successful movement environment.

When thinking about the segmental position, consider how motion is affected from the bottom up, as well as the top down. Imagine the spine as a spiral staircase that has vertical, rotational, and lateral components to it. However, instead of just a simple staircase, you will need to imagine it as the body moves and is impacted by pelvis and arm motion.

Think about the lumbar spine from a position in gait with the left foot and right arm forward, just prior to the right heel elevating off the ground as seen earlier in Photo 4.9. As the left leg swings forward, it "pulls" the left hip forward. As the left foot hits the ground and the foot pronates, the reaction causes the leg to internally rotate, and as our foundational concept dictates, we now have internal rotation of the left hip as the distal femur bone is internally rotated on the pelvis.

At the same time, the pelvis turns to the right, and as the pelvis is turned right, the sacrum is rotated right as well. The sacral facets of S-1 "carry" the fifth lumbar facets to the right, the fourth follows, and so on up the lumbar spine.

The right arm is forward in a contralateral reach, and the thoracic spine is rotated left as the right arm and shoulder are forward, causing the thoracic spine to be driven toward the left.

There will come a transition point when the lumbar spine rotates less to the right at each segment farther upward toward the thoracic spine, and the thoracic spine will move less to the left as it moves downward toward the lumbar spine. There is an imaginary rotational line from the right extended leg and hip that goes from the lower right quadrant up and toward the backward-extended left shoulder.

This extension and rotation causes these two endpoints to be farthest from each other, and allows the abdominals in the front to be eccentrically loaded from the right upward to the left. I call this the "Flexibility Highways Anterior X-Factor," which we will expand upon in Chapter Five, beginning on page 93.

Additionally, the left gluteal complex is lengthened as the left hip is flexed and internally rotated. When viewing the right latissimus dorsi and posterior shoulder girdle, the right posterior side is eccentrically loaded from the lower left hip up through the upper right shoulder. In this orientation, the lumbar spine is extended and rotated toward the left ilium in the sagittal and transverse planes.

These structures are connected via the lumbar fascia, forming the Flexibility Highways Posterior X-Factor, discussed more on page 104.

As the hip moves forward over the left foot during the mid-stance phase of gait, the right hip will drop a bit, causing the left to be higher.

In movement, the body will strive to keep the head and eyes level, similar to a bobblehead doll. If you tilt the body of a bobblehead doll, the head will shift to stay level. In humans, this accommodation is made through the spine. Therefore, the lumbar spine will laterally flex to the right. If this did not occur, the torso would lean to the opposite side of the higher hip—in this case, to the right. This frontal-plane reaction allows the body to remain relatively upright and stable.

Examine Photo 4.12 and Figure 4.3 and determine the vertebral segment positions in all three planes of motion.

As a review, the spine reacts to the gait stride in the following tri-plane motions—assuming left foot in the stride cycle:

- *Spinal flexion at left heel strike in the sagittal plane*
- *Spinal extension in relation to an extended hip in the sagittal plane prior to the right foot swinging through during the gait cycle*
- *Spinal rotation to the left in the transverse plane at left heel strike and mid-stance*
- *Lateral flexion to the left in the frontal plane during the right leg swing phase*

**PHOTO 4.12 LEFT LEG FORWARD WITH RIGHT ARM REACH, REAR VIEW**

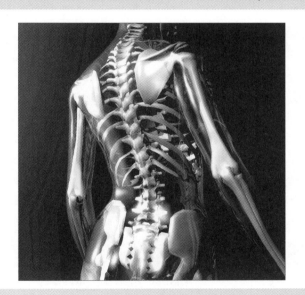

**FIGURE 4.3 VERTEBRAL SEGMENT POSITIONS**

## THE SHOULDER GIRDLE COMPLEX

Most often when healthcare and fitness professionals talk about shoulder function, they advise their clients to train the shoulder joint to be stable. This logic is correct to a point, as we want a stable shoulder joint, especially in those who participate in athletics such as baseball, softball, tennis, golf, javelin, and volleyball, just to name a few.

However, there are other issues that affect shoulder function we need to review.

The shoulder is the most mobile joint in the body and is dependent upon a mobile scapula. The scapula has 19 muscles that attach to it, and each one must be strong enough to withstand eccentric forces to allow the scapula to glide over the ribs in all three planes of motion. Scapular motion is necessary to create a successful shoulder joint environment.

The scapula is a "floating" bone influenced by body motions and, along with the shoulder girdle, moves in three planes of motion. Scapular reaction is typically an unconscious response to gravity, body position and angles, and segmental mobility.

Many shoulder impingement issues are a result of the scapula not properly gliding and not allowing the greater trochanter of the shoulder to be clear of the acromion process, especially during shoulder abduction moments. Impingement is often the result of the lack of scapular motion or timing of the scapula moving while the humerus abducts, causing a pinching of the supraspinatus tendon. This is a common cause of a shoulder injury.

However, we will not use this section to discuss the countless number of shoulder injuries, but to address the relationship of the scapula to the shoulder, as scapular reactions are a result of other body movements.

There is a saying I often use about shoulder function, "Where the scapula goes, the humerus will follow." Humeral motion is greatly affected by scapular reaction. Likewise, the scapula is affected by humeral actions.

However, if we step back from the shoulder girdle to observe the implications other parts of the body have on the scapula, we quickly sense that the scapula is dependent upon thoracic-spine movement.

If we delve deeper with a global perspective, the thoracic spine is impacted by motion of the lumbar spine, which is influenced by hip motion. The hips, as we have observed, are tremendously dependent on foot function. This indicates a distinct relationship of the hips and the scapula for us to explore.

Stop and imagine the important relationship between pelvic mobility and scapular motion. In the sagittal plane when there is adequate hip extension, the scapula will depress and slightly retract.

You can explore this by standing in a neutral, bilateral stance. Drive your hips forward, creating a relative hip extension of the hips to the spine. You will notice that the spine extends backward and the scapulae depress and retract—see Photo 4.13. This subconscious reaction is due to the change of body position and angles that allow the scapulae to react to gravitational forces, pulling them downward.

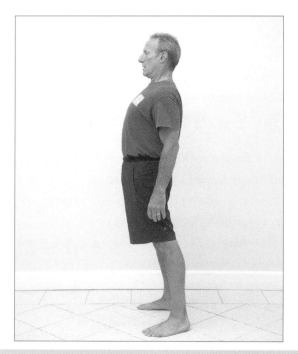

**PHOTO 4.13 SCAPULAR RETRACTION IN EXTENDED HIP POSTURE**

Next, keep the arms relaxed and flex the spine forward to allow hip flexion. Notice the scapulae are elevated and protracted as shown in Photo 4.14—again in response to body angles and gravity.

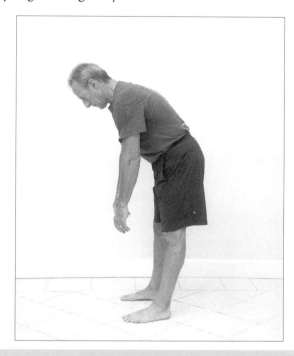

**PHOTO 4.14 SCAPULAR PROTRACTION IN FLEXED-FORWARD POSTURE**

Extrapolate how body angles and position changes might affect the scapula during a reach to an overhead cabinet. A person reaching extends at the hip to allow the lumbar and thoracic spine to extend, creating an environment for the scapula to depress, "clear" the acromion process in the sagittal plane, and for the shoulder joint to flex to accomplish the reach. If more upward stretch is required to reach a desired object overhead, the scapula will then upwardly rotate and protract to reach at a higher level.

Likewise, if that same person reaches to pick up something from the ground, the hips, lumbar, and thoracic spine will flex, causing the scapula to elevate and protract to allow the humerus to move.

Another example can be seen in bowling. As the bowler approaches a shot, we would see flexion at the hip and spine, which allows the scapula to elevate and retract while the shoulder joint extends. The reason for this slightly different reaction at the scapula is there is usually a small rotation of the thoracic spine as the bowler extends the shoulder during the backswing of the bowling motion. The rotation causes the scapula to retract.

None of these actions can be achieved efficiently, effectively, or safely without those synergistic responses.

Now, so you can feel the effect on the shoulder joint for yourself, try any of these movements, but do not allow the hips or spine to naturally move. You will notice the shoulder is not successful in the task and you may feel a "jamming" sensation. Over many repetitions or years of dysfunction, this "jamming" may lead to injury.

In the frontal plane, the same-side hip that adducts or abducts will cause the scapula of the corresponding side to adduct or abduct as seen in Photos 4.15 and 4.16. Also, the same-side hip that adducts will cause the same-side scapula to abduct. On the same side, the opposite joint that abducts will adduct on the opposite side.

**PHOTO 4.15 FRONTAL-PLANE SHOULDER ROTATOR CUFF ECCENTRICALLY LOADED THROUGH SHOULDER ABDUCTION**

**PHOTO 4.16 FRONTAL-PLANE SHOULDER ROTATOR CUFF CONCENTRICALLY LOADED THROUGH SHOULDER ADDUCTION**

We commonly see throwing injuries in the shoulder complex due to lack of motion in the transverse plane. There is a key relationship between the opposite hip and shoulder during throwing-like actions—golfing, tennis, hitting, racquetball, and throwing to name a few.

It is important for the opposite hip to attain a good range of motion during external rotation to allow the opposite shoulder to externally rotate. When that occurs, the torso typically turns away from the opposite hip and toward the side of the affected shoulder joint.

For example, when a right-handed thrower is in the act of throwing, the body turns toward the right hand and away from the left hip. This causes the right scapula to retract as it glides along the ribs. This is necessary to create clearance of the subacromial space, reducing the risk of impingement. Lack of motion in the opposite hip or shoulder through external rotation may not allow the throwing shoulder to be clear of the acromion process during a throwing-type motion.

Likewise, many posterior shoulder issues are a result of the inability to obtain adequate internal rotation of the opposite hip, which does not allow the leg, hip, and torso to efficiently decelerate the arm during follow-through. If that happens, the person is relying too much on the posterior shoulder musculature to decelerate the arm's action.

If there is not enough left-hip internal rotation for a right-handed thrower, the scapula will not be in a successful position in protraction and can cause improper arm-slot positioning during the deceleration phase of throwing. This is also true of other actions such as the follow-through in a golf swing or of a boxing motion such as a jab.

Based on that, we can describe the transverse-plane relationship of the hip through the torso to the shoulder girdle, especially the scapula. When the opposite hip has good range of motion into internal rotation, it will enhance opposite-shoulder internal rotation. Likewise, the opposite hip with good range of motion in external rotation will enhance opposite-shoulder external rotation.

Photos 4.17 and 4.18 show how the opposite hip must externally rotate to allow the scapula to be mobile and to retract, which will create successful shoulder-joint external rotation of the opposite shoulder. Likewise, the same-side hip must be able to attain adequate internal rotation to allow the same-side shoulder to externally rotate.

**PHOTO 4.17 OPPOSITE HIP AND SHOULDER ARE EXTERNALLY ROTATED. LIKEWISE, INTERNAL ROTATION OF THE SAME-SIDE HIP WILL ENHANCE EXTERNAL ROTATION OF THE SAME-SIDE SHOULDER.**

**PHOTO 4.18 OPPOSITE HIP AND SHOULDER ARE INTERNALLY ROTATED**

In throwing motions, these are the load-up and release phases. The release point will demonstrate the body moving into internal rotation of the hip opposite of the throwing arm and external rotation of the same-side hip—often referred to as the drive leg or hip—to allow protraction of the scapula and internal rotation of the opposite-side shoulder joint of the throwing arm.

I often work with pitchers who have had ulnar collateral ligament (UCL) injuries—in the past 18 months, I saw 20 referrals from orthopedic surgeons of pitchers with UCL injuries. After evaluating these players, I reviewed previous referrals of pitchers with this injury.

All of the pitchers with ulnar collateral injuries or UCL surgeries had tight hips of the lead leg of their delivery. For instance, with a right-handed pitcher, the left hip was tight into internal rotation. A normal range of motion of hip internal rotation is between 35–45 degrees. All of the injured pitchers had 30 degrees or less of internal rotation of the lead hip. There is a strong link between hip rotation and elbow injuries.

There must be mobility in various joint segments to allow the reactions to transpire, and also stability to control and decelerate all the reactions that simultaneously occur.

Sometimes people are either overly well-developed in the latissimus dorsi, hindering good rotation through the thoracic spine, or are immobile in the hips, inhibiting adequate motion to control the eccentric phase of the throwing motion. In these cases, they are *too* stable—not mobile enough to accommodate the necessary transverse- and frontal-plane actions required for rotary activities.

There are a multitude of maladies that can limit motion, creating instability in other areas of the body. As you gain this understanding, you will be able to help your clients create an environment for shoulder-joint success based on the status of the shoulder girdle, while also reflecting toward the lower-body segments.

To review the shoulder complex movement relationships:

- *In the sagittal plane, the same-side hip that flexes will enhance scapular elevation and slight retraction to allow shoulder-joint extension. Likewise, the same-side hip that extends creates an environment for the scapula to depress, protract, and slight upward rotation to enhance shoulder-joint flexion.*
- *In the frontal plane, the same-side hip that adducts or abducts will cause the scapula of the corresponding side to adduct or abduct.*
- *In the transverse plane, the opposite-side hip that externally rotates will cause the opposite scapula to glide on the ribs and retract, allowing the opposite-side shoulder joint to externally rotate. At the same time, the same-side hip will internally rotate to allow the same-side scapula to retract and the shoulder joint to externally rotate. Additionally, opposite-hip internal rotation will enhance opposite-shoulder internal rotation.*

One last point to consider: Make sure there is adequate motion of the sternoclavicluar joint and that the clavicle abducts in the frontal plane. If this region is tight, it will not allow the acromion process to optimally move and allow efficient shoulder abduction.

## THE CERVICAL SPINE—C-SPINE

Our discussion of movement has covered joints and structures impacting above and below the specified region. The cervical spine presents a slightly different perspective, as the majority of its motion is often a result of actions that impact the cervical spine from below. The cervical spine can often be likened to that bobblehead doll, as it is impacted by body positions, angles, and motions that have a relative impact on the C-spine.

The cervical spine is unique in that the lower portion from C3 through C7 should maintain its inherent lordosis to serve as a shock absorber from forces generated below.

The upper cervical spine—the cervico-occiptal—and the atlas do not have the ample tri-plane motion of the remaining segments. In order to preserve upper cervical-spine integrity, the lower cervical region requires this tri-plane motion. The atlas—C1—has no rotation or lateral flexion and functions primarily in the sagittal plane. Vertebrae C1 and C2 move in the sagittal plane with flexion, extension, and translation, but without lateral flexion.

The orientation of the cervical vertebrae has an alignment that places each segment at approximately a 45-degree angular articulation to each other. When the cervical spine flexes, there is a gliding forward or an opening of the proximal cervical segment on the distal segments.

Conversely, there is a closing of these segments relative to extension as the proximal segment moves back to the more neutral position or into extension. This can be considered not only flexion and extension, but also as a gliding translation over a center of rotation.

The upper cervical spine is typically conducive for flexion and extension, with limited lateral flexion and rotation. The lower cervical spine has more tri-plane actions; in fact, these actions require simultaneous motion in all three planes for successful movement.

Cervical rotation to the right will cause the transverse processes of the C-spine to turn to the right. Concomitantly, there is a slight lateral flexion to the right in the frontal plane, and extension of the transverse process. Motion must occur in all three planes to allow a successful movement. This does not include the posterior translation or the linear backward glide of a body part or a bone segment required during this action.

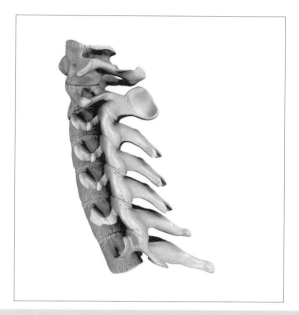

**FIGURE 4.4 OBSERVE THE 45-DEGREE ANGLE OF THE JOINTS OF THE CERVICAL SPINE**

Periodically, a client will present with a straight or flexed cervical spine. Review Photo 4.19 below to see the cervical spine flexed in a kyphotic posture.

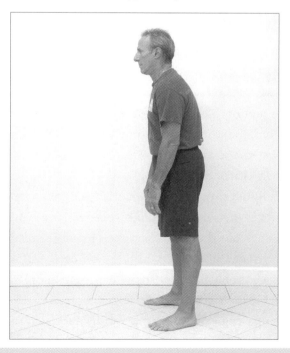

**PHOTO 4.19 KYPHOTIC POSTURE**

People in our field generally have addressed this in an isolated manner. But if you step back to analyze the impact the body has on the cervical spine, you will notice how the body's posture has affected the cervical spine.

Assuming the cause is more soft tissue related than a degenerative joint disease of the cervical region, the majority of cases who present with a flat cervical spine have flexed thoracic and lumbar spines. If we look distally, the pelvis typically is in a posterior-tilted position.

To functionally improve the cervical spine, the lumbar spine must accomplish a relatively extended position to gain lordosis, which will allow the thoracic spine increased extension. This will create an environment for the cervical spine to be in a lordotic position to allow motion to occur.

One successful strategy to help with this is to have the person stand in a staggered stance and drive the hips forward as shown in Photo 4.20. This allows the extended hip to anteriorly tilt. The lumbar spine will extend in relation to the hip; the thoracic spine will extend; the scapula will retract along with the shoulder girdle; the head will retract and the cervical spine will be in an environment to regain its lordosis.

Next, have the client posteriorly reach at hip height with the same-side arm of the forward hip. This retracts the scapula and enhances postural alignment.

**PHOTO 4.20 LEFT LEG FORWARD WITH SAME-SIDE ARM EXTENSION**

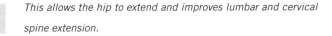

*This allows the hip to extend and improves lumbar and cervical spine extension.*

Tell the client to imagine there is a flashlight in the navel, hence the "Beacon of Life." When performing rotational motions, use the cue to "Shine the light" so the pelvis rotates. If the pelvis rotates, the lumbar spine will follow. Make sure the person rotates into the lead hip to shine the "Beacon of Life" toward that hip.

If the hips are tight and rotation is difficult, assess why the hips are tight, and develop a strategy to progressively mobilize them.

**PHOTO 4.21 SHINE THE BEACON OF LIGHT— WHERE THE PELVIS GOES, THE LOW BACK WILL FOLLOW**

To review the cervical region, consider the following concepts:

- *Movement involves all three planes of motion.*
- *When movement occurs, there is a translation of the vertebral segments over the center of rotation.*
- *Look for adequate motion within the thoracic spine for successful cervical movement.*

## THINKING THROUGH A THREE-DIMENSIONAL APPROACH

Human motion is a complex synergy of tri-plane segmental actions that work to accomplish a specific task. The reactions to those segmental motions are necessary for efficient and economical results.

To fully assist our clients, we need to develop strategies that address their movement problems, not the symptoms.

People in our field do a marvelous job of addressing the "what," "when," and "how" of program design. If a client has a knee problem, people often expect to address it (the "what") by doing certain exercises, either with machines or bodyweight (the "how"), and plan this approach in a certain sequence of events (the "when").

However, these trainers often fail to address the "why." If a client has an injury issue, particularly if it is an overuse problem, the site of the injury is not the problem—it is the symptom. The problem is typically a joint one or two levels above or below the symptom. The symptom is merely the site of the discomfort.

We must step back and learn how the body moves through a three-dimensional approach and look at movement from a global perspective, not just a local one. When this paradigm is embraced, program design will take an entirely different construction, and we will create truly personalized exercise prescriptions that address the limitations, compensations, and idiosyncrasies of each of our clients.

Take the time to absorb this material. Be persistent. It will pay off in the long run, and ultimately this knowledge will have a great impact on the lives of those you serve.

# FLEXIBILITY HIGHWAYS—THE ROAD TO ENHANCED FUNCTIONAL PERFORMANCE

*"Blessed are the flexible,*
*for they will not be bent out of shape."*

~ M I C H A E L   M C G R I F F E Y ,   MD

In earlier years, flexibility was always an afterthought of a training program, and isolation was the traditionally accepted mode of stretching. There is nothing wrong with isolated stretching, but we must remember this is only a "link" action that targets a single muscle or set of muscle tissue, not the "chain" action that resonates in a body.

The study of fascia has recently gained much attention in the fitness and rehabilitation worlds. It is a fascinating field that deserves consideration when designing exercise programs for our various clients.

Remember the common mantra of fitness and medical professionals who study movement: The site of the injury is not the problem—often it is a joint level or two away from the compensation. The appreciation of fascial principles aligns with this concept; consideration of the fascial webbing brings an understanding of how improper movement patterns inhibit fascial gliding.

Using the analogy of a sweater with a snag in its woven pattern, you can picture that the sweater does not lie correctly and feels tight somewhere in the fit. If there is a snag in the lower left area of the sweater, it may cause the stitches to pull and stretch toward the opposite shoulder. The opposite shoulder may feel tight, and we may pull on the sweater to stretch out the restriction felt at the shoulder.

This is a symptom that is felt; it is not the underlying problem. If the snagged area at the lower left is addressed and fixed, the sweater will lie well and the opposite shoulder region will not feel tight.

The same concept often applies in the fascial system. If movement is not efficient, "snagging" can take place in the fascial tissue and can cause symptoms elsewhere in the body. The appreciation of human movement, along with our attempt to study the fascial system, can be a powerful tool in the toolbox to provide the relieving remedy to optimal motion.

As Ida Rolf, the creator of Rolfing, states in *Endless Web*, a book by R. Louis Schultz and Rosemary Feitis:

*"What at first is a way to protect a part of the body (particularly a part that hurts) eventually results in a loss of fluidity throughout the entire body."*

## UNIVERSAL CONNECTIONS: ESSENTIALS OF FASCIAL PROPERTIES

Fascia is the universal webbing connecting all body tissue. It provides a unified, synergistic network for efficient and economical movement. Fascia allows the tissue, especially muscle, to do useful work, but not at the expense of tissue overload.

Fascia transmits and mitigates forces from internal and external loads. It creates a unified network of longitudinal, latitudinal, and in-depth connections, so muscle and other soft tissue can generate a useful outcome with the least amount of stress to the myoskeletal system.

There are basically three different types of fascial fibers: collagen, elastin, and reticulin.

Reticulin is the immature collagen fiber largely found in embryos and infants, which changes into collagen as a child matures into an adult.

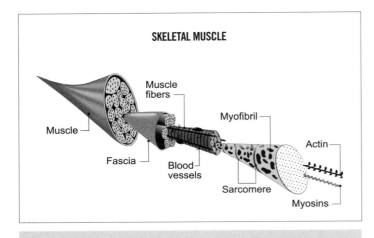

**SKELETAL MUSCLE**

**FIGURE 5.1 MUSCLE FIBERS**

Reticulin (immature collagen) is gradually replaced by collagen produced by mesodermal fibroblasts, comprising the sticky extracellular matrix.

Looking at the smallest unit of soft tissue, the actin and myosin filaments are held together by fascia. The cross-bridges connect to the Z-lines, while fascia forms the structure to keep the tissue aligned.

When muscle tissue contracts and the cross-bridges articulate, fascia holds the filaments and maintains the essential space to allow these filaments to glide over each other.

The smallest contractile unit is the sarcomere, identified from Z-line to Z-line. The Z-line defines the borders of the sarcomere, thereby attaching adjacent sarcomere. The actin filaments, which are the thin filaments, attach to the Z-lines. The Z-line is held together by fascial tissue. Multiple sarcomeres make up the filaments that attach to

other filaments, forming the muscle bundle—all unified by fascia.

Muscle bundles attach to adjacent muscle bundles to form the belly of the muscle tissue, held together by fascia. These form into endomysium, epimysium, and perimysium, and are all coupled together by fascia.

The connection of the muscle to bone and the ligamentous tissue connecting bone to bone are made up of fascial tissue. The universal connection of fascia is everywhere in the body, all designed to assist with movement, absorbing and transmitting force, and adapting to the task at hand.

## EXTRACELLULAR MATRIX (ECM)

The life cycle and aging process are miraculous transformations, although as we get older, we sometimes find that frustrating. Watching infants play, twist, turn, and effortlessly contort themselves makes adults reminisce about the days they could do those marvelous feats of mobility.

The reason children have this ability is due to the very pliable reticulin, which allows incredible motion. As humans mature, the reticulin is replaced by the mature collagen, which favors stability. Collagen is the structure comprising fascia, which is nourished by a gluey, sticky substance known as extracellular matrix (ECM).

This ECM is identified as glycosaminoglycans (GAGs) and proteoglycans. According to *Gray's Anatomy*:

> *"The term extracellular matrix (ECM)…essentially consists of a system of insoluble protein fibrils and soluble complexes composed of carbohydrate polymers linked to protein molecules (i.e., proteoglycans) which bind water. Mechanically, the ECM has evolved to distribute the stresses of movement and gravity while at the same time maintaining the shape of the different components of the body."*

Think of this concept as similar to a large waterbed. When a person sits on one end of the bed, the water is displaced to other regions, thereby reducing the full load and force of the seated person and transferring it to other parts of the bed.

In the body, force applied to the system can cause excessive wear and tissue breakdown over time. The ECM produces a transfer of those forces and distributes them through the system to create an efficient "off-loading" of the forces from one region to share the load.

## WHAT HAPPENS WHEN FASCIA IS STIMULATED

Fascia is *stimulated by mechanical loading and is strengthened by eccentric loading.* It is constantly adapting to the environment of forces and stresses within and applied to body tissues. Fascia has a high tolerance to resist forces and slowly adjusts or creeps as its length changes. As the tissues adjust to the forces and demands on them, the fascia will slowly lengthen with muscle tissue to control and decelerate motion. As this happens, the fascia will become stronger, particularly when it is eccentrically loaded in three planes of motion.

For example, consider patients who have had an ankle, knee, or hip injury or surgery. Part of the return-to-play process is not only the strengthening phase, but also improving mobility. Invariably, due to the injury and inflammation cycle and the accompanying immobilization, the joint gets tight, the soft tissue shortens, and the overall quality of movement becomes limited.

This new weakness is not only from lack of use and atrophy, but also from lack of motion through the joint segments and the associated chain reaction of motion in the adjacent joints. In essence, this lack of mobility is the body's compensation to protect the joint and surrounding tissues from further damage. This cycle must be broken to allow ample motion and strength gains for recovery and progression.

We do not want to build stability on top of stability. In those scenarios of those who have had injury, the joints are *too* stable. Many associate stability with strength.

However, when looking at functional tri-plane motion, too much stability limits proper tri-plane mobility, which inhibits optimal loading of the joint structures and soft tissues. This reduces the eccentric loading capabilities in all three planes of motion, and ultimately reduces strength.

Our goal is to first regain mobility of the soft tissues and joints in a tri-plane environment. Initially, deep tissue work by a skilled physical therapist or massage therapist can help mobilize the joints and break down the limitations related to fascial stickiness or adhesions.

Additionally, by having the client perform remedial movement patterns under bodyweight, not only will you see a gain in range of motion, this person will also gain strength and be able to progress in a safe and efficient manner.

Movement constantly remodels the extracellular matrix that comprises fascial tissue. All postural positions require the fascial system to maintain the postural structure. If collagen assists in maintaining the structure yet movement modifies the fascial consistency, we can say that collagen favors mobility. This will enhance the eccentric loading of tissue, resulting in stability of the tissue and joints.

To attain the optimal loading, we must load in tri-plane positions for adaptation.

## THE FLEXIBILITY HIGHWAYS

Many dysfunctions, pains, and musculoskeletal symptoms result from muscle tightness, joint tightness, and especially from fascial "stickiness," more commonly called tightness. Recent research by Thomas Myers of *Anatomy Trains* has found that fascia possesses nine or ten times more proprioceptors than muscle tissue. These range-of-motion limitations lead to a chain reaction of compensations that cause overuse of some muscle tissue and lack of use of the prime movers. However, significant improvements can occur after a series of thoughtful stretching.

Flexibility is one of the most controversial components of fitness. By definition, flexibility is the range of motion over a joint or series of joints. Yet, that definition neglects the effects of muscle tightness on other muscular structures, and ignores the fact that flexibility takes on a new paradigm when joints, fascia, and muscles move in three planes of motion.

We must broaden our thinking of stretching programs to incorporate three-dimensional stretching of soft tissue through the sagittal, frontal, and transverse planes. Additionally, there must be a chain-link relationship from one muscle group to an adjacent muscle group when performing a biomechanically sound stretching program.

Tradition has reinforced that muscle flexibility should be single-joint and single-plane actions. It is a more functional approach to incorporate multiple joints and planes into what I call, "The Flexibility Highways" stretch, as this is more conducive to actual human motion. I first devised the Flexibility Highways concept in 2000.

For example, to functionally stretch the abdominals, it is important for the hip flexors to be included in the stretch, as hip-flexor flexibility will add to the motion of the abdominals and torso extension in the sagittal plane. When dynamic extension actions occur in the sagittal plane, the abdominals and hip flexors must accommodate adequate excursion of these muscles to optimally perform in human motion.

Interestingly, the chain reactions of adjacent extremities affect joints above and below the muscles as we stretch. When the abdominals and hip flexors are stretched from a standing position, it is important to have the same-side heel on the ground. We also need a good range of motion in the same-side calf group, because the soleus and gastrocnemius work synergistically to extend the knee in the sagittal plane and to control rotation of the knee in the transverse plane. The interplay of these adjacent muscles is just an example of the integrated relationship myofascia has in human motion.

Likewise, muscles responsible for the control of transverse-plane actions should be concurrently stretched, as these muscles work synergistically to control the rotational action. If these muscles and fascia are stretched together, the stretching of the myofascia and stimulation of the myofascial proprioceptors is enhanced through motions reminiscent of an action.

Additionally, when stretching an upper extremity such as the shoulder joint, it is critical to understand what plane of motion you are trying to increase. From a functional motion perspective, the hips play an integral part in shoulder action, and thus need to be incorporated into the stretch as well.

For example, when stretching the shoulder in the sagittal plane, it is important to stretch the same-side hip in the sagittal plane at the same time. When the shoulder flexes, sufficient hip extension on the same side must accompany that movement to prevent overuse of the shoulder musculature.

In the frontal plane, the hip abductors and adductors must have enough flexibility to enhance shoulder-girdle and shoulder-joint adduction and abduction.

In the transverse plane, optimal shoulder external rotation is dependent upon the opposite hip internal rotators being flexible, along with the same-side hip external rotators.

And with all shoulder motion, there must be adequate flexibility in the scapular and parascapular muscles to allow movement of the scapula over the thoracic cage.

## THE SIX FLEXIBILITY HIGHWAYS

To expand on those concepts, we categorize flexibility programming into six highways:

- *The Anterior Flexibility Highway*
- *The Posterior Flexibility Highway*
- *The Lateral Flexibility Highway*
- *The Anterior X-Factor Flexibility Highway*
- *The Posterior X-Factor Flexibility Highway*
- *The Turnpike*

We will cover those now, and you will also find an overview of these Highways for reference in Appendix One on page 209.

The logic behind the Flexibility Highways concept is to use the chain-reaction premise that fascia, muscles, and joints are influenced by adjacent fascia, muscles, and joints. In this sense, to improve range of motion, we work from the ground up and integrate the myofascial relationship along the appropriate "highway."

When reviewing the anatomy of each Highway, think of the myofascial attachments of one group and the adjacent myofascia as interchanges on an interstate highway. When one structure or "street" ends, it conjoins or interchanges with the next structure or street.

## THE ANTERIOR FLEXIBILITY HIGHWAY

The Anterior Flexibility Highway runs from the south to the north—from the bottom to the top of the body—or along the sagittal plane. Flexion and extension movements occur along this Highway.

The myofascial tissues of this Highway begin at the dorsal surface of the foot with the toe extensors and interchange with the anterior compartment of the ankle and tibia. This runs from the anterior tibialis upward, connecting to the distal quadriceps near the patellar tendon.

The next interchange north is the patellar tendon and the quadriceps attachment toward the hip flexors. To enhance function of both the quadriceps and hip flexors, it is important to lengthen both structures together.

The hip flexors intersect with the abdominals that travel to the ribs, sternum, and the sternochondral fascia, and then venture into the pectorals, anterior shoulder, and the sternocleidomastoid.

From there, an angular detour takes our journey to the mastoid process of the Anterior Flexibility Highway, which enhances extension movements.

Please refer to Figure 5.2 to see the Anterior Flexibility Highway and the relationships of the adjoining tissues.

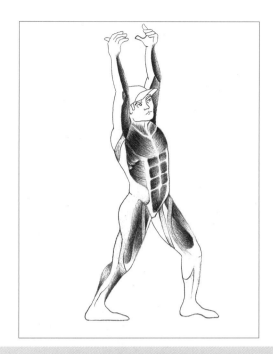

**FIGURE 5.2 THE ANTERIOR FLEXIBILITY HIGHWAY**

Following this concept, you can see that the range of motion in the southern section of the Highway can affect the northern section.

Photos 5.1 and 5.2 demonstrate integrated stretching to enhance the range of motion along the anterior aspect of the body.

Photos 5.1 and 5.2 demonstrate level one of the Anterior Flexibility Highway. Level one has four points of contact with both feet on the ground and both hands holding on to a stable structure. This is performed with the foot of the extended hip firmly on the ground. It is very important to keep the heel on the ground as this will stretch the calf on the same side.

You have seen that the same-side calf and hip flexor need to be stretched together. Ankle dorsiflexion must be present to allow the hip to fully extend. If either the hip flexor or calf group is tight, it will negatively affect the other region, lowering the ability to rotate to the opposite side.

Photo 5.3 shows a deeper hip flexor stretch of the Anterior Flexibility Highway. This is more challenging, as it requires increased stability because there are only three points of contact. In the photo, the right hip is extended and the left foot is on the ground, while both arms hold onto the stable structure.

Level two allows more hip extension, however. If the client has limited hip mobility or significant anterior pelvic tilt, I discourage this stretch as it may cause a "jamming" at the L-5/S1 facets in the lumbar spine.

**PHOTO 5.1 ANTERIOR FLEXIBILITY HIGHWAY STRETCH, LEVEL ONE, SIDE VIEW**

*Notice how the same heel is in contact with the ground to stretch the calf. This will improve the hip flexor stretch as well. If either tissue is tight, it will affect the other.*

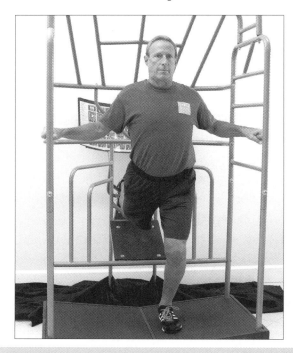

**PHOTO 5.3 ANTERIOR FLEXIBILITY HIGHWAY, LEVEL TWO, FRONT VIEW**

**PHOTO 5.2 ANTERIOR FLEXIBILITY HIGHWAY, LEVEL ONE, REAR VIEW**

**PHOTO 5.4 ANTERIOR FLEXIBILITY HIGHWAY, LEVEL TWO WITH ARM REACH**

Photo 5.4 displays a level-two stretch with the right arm reaching to left lateral. This option will increase the stretch from the hip flexors into the obliques and abdominals. The close fascial connection of these tissues becomes stretched with this opposite lateral reach. If the left hip flexor is being stretched, place the left arm to the right for the same effect on the left side.

In many of the exercises using the True Stretch, you may substitute a box, bench, step, or chair if you do not have a True Stretch unit available. If using something in lieu of it, make sure you place that item in an area that allows the client to hold on to something stable, such as a counter, grab bars or something solid. This allows the client to do the Flexibility Highway stretches with three or four points of contact, depending upon whether holding with one or two hands.

You can also do these on flat ground and imitate the positions shown in the photos.

## THE POSTERIOR FLEXIBILITY HIGHWAY

Like the Anterior Highway, the Posterior Flexibility Highway runs from the south to the north or along the sagittal plane, but with flexion movements along this length. The myofascia of this Highway begins at the plantar surface of the foot from the toe flexors, moves through the posterior compartment of the foot and ankle, meeting at the Achilles tendon. Through the posterior calf group of the gastrocnemius, flexor digitorum, soleus, and posterior tibialis northward, the knee interchange meets the hamstrings.

The gastrocnemius attaches at the femoral condyles and conjoins with the descending hamstrings that attach at the tibial condyles. In fact, the gastrocnemius and hamstrings connect with each other, forming the "trapeze artists of the body."

The hamstrings attach below and around the knee on the tibial condyles. The hamstrings run north, attaching at the ischial tuberosity and merging into the sacrotuberous ligament. In this region, a major interchange emerges as the sacrotuberous ligament meets the lumbosacral fascia, and passes into the gluteal complex and the erector spinae.

The erector group travels north to connect with the occiput and conjoins with the epicranial fascia at the forehead.

It is important that the union of the gluteals and the erector spinae musculature be stretched in an integrated fashion, as any functional lumbar movement pattern includes the gluteals. Due to that relationship, these structures should be developed together.

The final posterior journey terminates at the scalp fascia.

Please see Figure 5.3 to appreciate the tissue connection along the Posterior Flexibility Highway.

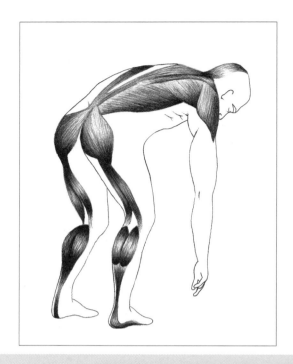

**FIGURE 5.3 THE POSTERIOR FLEXIBILITY HIGHWAY**

**PHOTO 5.5 THE POSTERIOR FLEXIBILITY HIGHWAY, WITH THE FEET ROTATED OUTWARD**

Photos 5.5 and 5.6 demonstrate the Posterior Flexibility Highway stretch. Photo 5.5 demonstrates integrated stretching to enhance range of motion along the posterior aspect of the body.

Adequate range of motion of the Posterior Flexibility Highway will enhance flexion movements.

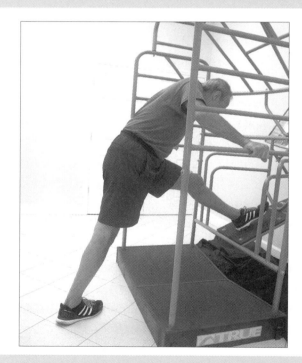

**PHOTO 5.6 THE POSTERIOR FLEXIBILITY HIGHWAY, WITH THE FEET ROTATED INWARD**

As noted, the hamstrings attach at the ischial tuberosities and then merge with the sacrotuberous ligament. The fascial network within the pelvic girdle makes up a pelvic ring when viewed from above. Notice the different positions of the right foot in the photos. The change of foot position causes a tensioning around the pelvic ring and therefore a greater stretch on different areas within the hamstrings.

Photo 5.5 has the right foot rotated to the right and the left leg rotating to the left. This places more tension on the medial side of the hamstrings and also affects the neighboring adductor group.

Photo 5.6 shows the right foot rotated to the left and the left foot rotated right. Considering the fascial connections of these structures, this positioning increases the tensioning along the lateral hamstrings complex into the gluteal complex.

When performing these stretches, we rotate the leg of the hamstrings being stretched right and left, similar to a windshield wiper. This will provide a tri-plane hamstrings stretch that will enhance movements such as a drop step—as when an outfielder is in the "ready" position and suddenly opens up the right hip to run to the right—when doing a stretch as in Photo 5.5 or a crossover step when stretched as in Photo 5.6.

**PHOTO 5.7 THE POSTERIOR X-FACTOR**

If you want to take a diversion through the rear shoulder group, a slight change of position and arm placement will include this area as well. Refer to Photo 5.7 for this alternative route. This will be discussed more in the section covering the Posterior X-Factor beginning on page 104.

## THE LATERAL FLEXIBILITY HIGHWAY

The Lateral Flexibility Highway is commonly overlooked in discussions on function. The Lateral Flexibility Highway runs from the south to the north along the frontal plane, with abduction and adduction movements occurring along this line.

Running from the lateral ankle and the peroneal group, the Lateral Highway goes north to the lateral tibial condyle and the iliotibial band. Moving upward from this taut structure, the IT band merges with the tensor fascia lata, the gluteus medius and minimus, and then meets with the gluteus maximus.

After analyzing the multidirectional fibrous "routes" of the gluteal complex, we know to include these sections of the Highways with *all* Flexibility Highway stretching. The gluteals are the "command central" of our center of gravity, balance, and power. They are used in all functional movement patterns, thus are the hub of tri-plane movement.

Along the Lateral Flexibility Highway, the lateral gluteals are adjacent to the quadratus lumborum and then the obliques. The obliques merge with the external and internal intercostals toward the anterior aspect and the latissimus dorsi in the posterior aspect. Additionally, these structures are close neighbors of the transverse abdominis by way of fascial anatomy.

From this point north, the lats will meet up with the posterior rotator cuff. There is a bypass at the junction of the latissimus dorsi and the trapezius group, whereby the journey northbound traverses through the trapezius group to the sternocleidomastoid.

Please refer to Figure 5.4 to appreciate the connections of the Lateral Flexibility Highway.

**FIGURE 5.4 THE LATERAL FLEXIBILITY HIGHWAY**

As Photo 5.8 demonstrates, stretching the Lateral Highway is necessary for enhancement of frontal-plane movement patterns.

**PHOTO 5.8 THE LATERAL FLEXIBILITY HIGHWAY**

For an optimal lateral stretch, think from the bottom up and let the hip move laterally as far as it can without undue strain. Additionally, the first metatarsal head of the foot on the stretched hip should be stable on the ground. This allows the tibia and femur to internally rotate and optimize the frontal-plane stretch of the Lateral Flexibility Highway into the hip.

The Lateral Flexibility Highway often becomes limited in motion among the sedentary population. This is frequently due to lack of motion elsewhere in the body, such as the foot and ankle complex. If that region is not producing proper motion, the tibia medial internal rotation is reduced, thereby causing a lack of femur medial rotation. If this happens, there will be reduced motion into adduction in the frontal plane of the affected hip.

Those who have suffered injury, whether from trauma or a surgical procedure, frequently display lack of motion along the Lateral Flexibility Highway. Those with a foot or ankle injury, knee or hip injury or surgery, back pain, and even shoulder immobility often suffer from tightness and lack of motion along this Highway.

To produce optimal function, it is critical to regain the mobility along the Lateral Flexibility Highway. If motion is reduced in the frontal plane, especially at the hip complex, the transverse plane into internal hip rotation will be adversely impacted.

## THE X-FACTORS FLEXIBILITY HIGHWAYS

The X-Factors Flexibility Highways consist of the Anterior X-Factor and Posterior X-Factor running from the south to the north along the transverse plane, with rotational movements occurring on these Highways. These Highways produce the most power and are the most functional in movement. They essentially affect all of the other four Highways.

The X-factors are the most complex of the Flexibility Highway systems because all routes can join one another. When analyzing movement patterns, remember that nothing happens in only one plane of motion. There is influence from one plane into the other two, yet often one plane is predominant.

We begin at the ground. From the navicular, cuneiform, and the second through the fifth metatarsals of the plantar surface of the foot, the posterior tibialis enters the posterior compartment of the tibia. The peroneus longus circles its wagons from the first metatarsal and medial cuneiform to the lateral fibular condyle, and later meets up with the biceps femoris. Additionally, the anterior tibialis from the first metatarsal comes around the bend to the lateral upper two-thirds of the tibia.

Upward along the posterior tibia to the knee, the biceps femoris travels to the ischial tuberosity. The gluteals emanate in a tri-plane fashion and circle laterally to the gluteus medius and minimus and the tensor fascia lata (TFL). Here the iliotibial band conjoins with the TFL.

Interestingly, the peroneals meet the iliotibial band at the knee and create a distant relationship with the lateral hip complex of the gluteals and TFL.

## THE ANTERIOR X-FACTOR

All motions involving rotation and extension run along the Anterior X-Factor (AXF). When viewing the anatomy of the adductors to the opposite pectoral and shoulder region, there is a somewhat parallel line along these tissues. This Flexibility Highway runs from the adductor insertion on the linea aspera on the posterior femur and originates at the pubic ramus of the pelvis.

There is a close fascial relationship between the origin of the adductors to the rectus abdominis as it traverses along the abdominals to the opposite intercostals and obliques, upward to the serratus anterior, into the pectorals, and into the opposite shoulder complex. Therefore, any motion that involves extension and rotation of the opposite side runs along the Anterior X-Factor as seen in Photo 5.9.

**PHOTO 5.9 THE ANTERIOR X-FACTOR IN ACTION**

*The left hip is in external rotation along with the right shoulder. A line from the left adductor through the abdominals to the right pectorals into the shoulder girdle forms the Anterior X-Factor and enhances extension with external rotation.*

If a person abducts and extends an arm, similar to a throwing motion or a golfer's backswing, the tissue from the deltoid into the biceps and forearm is included in the Anterior X-Factor.

It is crucial to possess ample mobility in the adductors, abdominals, and pectoral regions to enhance motions through the AXF. Likewise, it is important to maintain good range of motion in the hamstrings, as these tissues are the "neighbor" of the adductors, and highly affect them. Using our understanding of the fascial lines, we know if the hamstrings are close friends to the AXF, the calf group must be as well, because the gastrocnemius and hamstrings are connected at the posterior knee.

There is a junction to one of the other Highways at many joints in the Flexibility Highways system. Please look at Figure 5.5 to appreciate the fascial lines of the Anterior X-Factor.

**FIGURE 5.5 THE ANTERIOR X-FACTOR**

To demonstrate the need to stretch the AXF in a unified approach, consider the actions of a throwing athlete such as a pitcher at the start of a windup in the throwing motion. As a right-handed pitcher's right arm extends back during the windup or cocking phase, the left hip moves into an externally rotated position from the torso.

When looking at the global action, the left hip is rotated outward, while the torso is turned to the right. The right arm and shoulder are abducted and extended away from the torso, and create a line from the left hip through the abdominal complex and into the right shoulder complex. You saw this in Photo 5.9.

The general action is rotation and extension, which are the key reactions through the Anterior X-Factor. A similar reaction occurs during the backswing of a right-handed golfer.

## THE POSTERIOR X-FACTOR

As you view the posterior architecture of the soft tissue, which we are calling the Posterior X-Factor (PXF), notice the nearly parallel line between the opposite gluteal complex and the latissimus dorsi. Both tissues entwine into the lumbosacral fascia, thereby joining the opposite hip and shoulder.

The importance of the PXF comes into play during flexion and rotational actions, such as the follow-through in a throw, the backswing during a golf swing, the follow-through of a tennis swing, or simply picking up an object within reach and lateral to you.

Please refer to Figure 5.6 to consider the tissues forming the Posterior X-Factor.

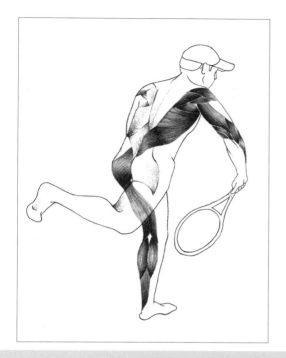

**FIGURE 5.6 THE POSTERIOR X-FACTOR**

Take a look at Photo 5.10 and envision the Posterior X-Factor myofascial system.

**PHOTO 5.10 THE POSTERIOR X-FACTOR**

*As the pitcher follows through, there is lengthening of the Posterior X-Factor through the hamstrings into the gluteal complex, through the lumbosacral fascia into the opposite latissimus dorsi to the shoulder to the arm. These tissues are eccentrically loaded to decelerate the follow-through action of a throw.*

Photos 5.11 and 5.12 demonstrate Anterior and Posterior X-Factor stretches.

In Photo 5.11, the hips are forward so the trail leg is extended and abducted. When people are tight, they often flex forward, thereby reducing the stretch at the hip. If an adductor is tight, often the knee will flex and the femur rotates slightly medially.

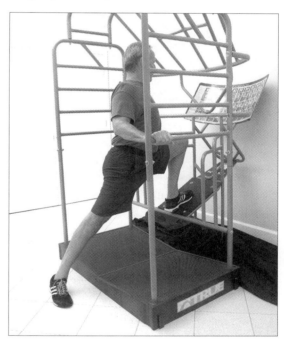

**PHOTO 5.11 THE ANTERIOR X-FACTOR WITH ADDUCTOR EMPHASIS**

In Photo 5.12, the right gluteal complex is stretched, along with the left latissimus dorsi. When performing this stretch, we push with the right arm and simultaneously pull with the left arm to increase the tension for a more intense stretch of the PXF. We do the opposite when stretching through the left-side Posterior X-Factor.

**PHOTO 5.12 THE POSTERIOR X-FACTOR**

*The hip complex is one of the main junctions of the highway system due to the many muscles that converge in this region. Here we see mergers of the Anterior, Posterior, and Lateral Highways in and around the hip. When looking at human motion, we can readily see how one of the other Flexibility Highways is also affected when stretching the X-factors. The hip complex is one of those major junctions that must be stretched in all three planes of motion.*

In movement, we keep a very important principle at the forefront of our strategies: *The two most mobile regions of the body are the hip complex and thoracic spine.*

This principle becomes evident through the X-factors because a rotational action is an integral aspect of these Flexibility Highways. If there is inadequate motion available in either the hips or the thoracic spine, compensating rotation will occur in the lumbar spine.

This is potentially detrimental to spine health, as available rotation in the lumbar spine is only approximately 13–15 degrees in the transverse plane. Try to gain motion in all three planes of movement in the hips and thoracic spine prior to working through the Anterior and Posterior X-Factor Highways.

## THE TURNPIKE

This unique system forms a relationship with the cervical spine and the hip via the opposite shoulder girdle. Running from the opposite scalene and capitis cervicis, these tissues conjoin with the rhomboids on the same side. The rhomboids attach to both scapulae, but due to the angulation of the rhomboids, this tissue attaches to the opposite scapula. The rhomboid runs laterally to connect with the subscapularis approximately one-third of the way from the medial border of the scapula.

The subscapularis travels laterally to merge with the serratus anterior about 20 percent from the lateral border. The serratus anterior wraps around the side of the body, connecting with the pectorals and external obliques.

The external oblique runs on an angle toward the linea alba of the rectus abdominis to the opposite hip. This Turnpike creates the indirect attachment from the same-side posterior cervical spine to the opposite shoulder, and diagonally back to the same-side hip on the anterior side.

Please see Figure 5.7 to appreciate the fascial tissue lines forming the Turnpike.

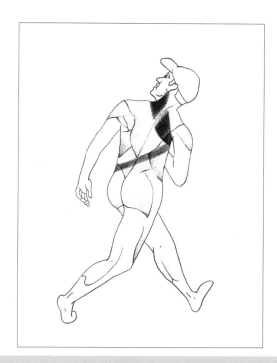

**FIGURE 5.7 THE TURNPIKE**

The importance of this Flexibility Highway comes into play when an activity requires the left hand to hold an object overhead, while at the same time the person is reaching with the right hand. If you hold a box on a shelf with the left hand and reach behind to grab another object with your right hand, the Turnpike comes into play to allow this action.

Imagine an athlete running downfield, and then turning the head to look over a shoulder to catch a ball. The thrown ball is slightly overhead and the athlete must reach forward to catch the ball. The Turnpike makes this task possible.

It is important to stretch and train clients through this movement pattern to mobilize the cervical spine, thoracic spine, shoulder girdle, and hips.

Please view Photos 5.13 and 5.14 for impressions of how movement impacts the Turnpike.

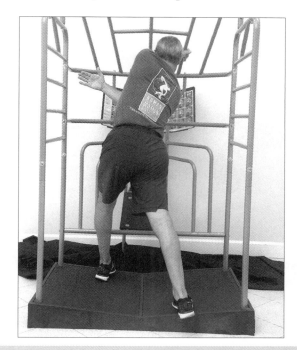

**PHOTO 5.13 THE TURNPIKE, TYPE I**

*The Type I Turnpike is characterized by thoracic rotation to one side while laterally flexed to the opposite side. In this photo, observe the left thoracic rotation and right lateral flexion of the thoracic spine. This is a Type I thoracic spine pattern.*

**PHOTO 5.14 THE TURNPIKE, TYPE II**

*The Type II Turnpike is characterized by thoracic rotation to one side while laterally flexed to the same side. In this photo, observe the right thoracic rotation and slight right lateral flexion of the thoracic spine. This is a Type II thoracic spine pattern.*

The uniqueness of this Flexibility Highway is that its success is highly dependent upon the Lateral and X-Factor Flexibility Highways. Each depends on the others to make these motions successful, especially in dynamic movement patterns.

## FLEXIBILITY HIGHWAYS IN MOTION

When I first developed the concept of Flexibility Highways, I had excellent success in assisting those with an immobility that impacted optimal performance.

Performance is a generic term specific to the designated task for each person. A performance task may range from daily activities, to work-related issues, to athletic functions. Performance is the blending of the client's wants—improved strength, hypertrophy, weight loss or gain, or proficiency at a specific task—with the person's needs, such as greater range of motion in the hips, mobilization of the subtalar joint, or scapular mobilization. The wants and needs do not always match, but as an intuitive trainer, you will be able to blend the wants and needs into an efficient and effective program.

I once made a mistake when working with a 70-year-old woman who was six months post-op after a hip replacement. She walked in to the clinic with a limp, causing her to have a gait similar to Trendelenburg sign. This is not unusual after hip replacement, as the lateral gluteal complex becomes weak and tight due to the surgical procedure and ensuing adhesions.

After successfully gaining range of motion, this energetic woman walked out with less control than when she walked in. I had failed her. She said her hip felt weaker—"mushy" was the word she used—and she was very concerned. I had assisted her toward greater hip motion, but failed to give her an appropriate movement pattern that would help her control the increased range of motion. Since the tissues were lengthened, the proprioceptors were also elongated, but she did not have the kinesthetic awareness nor the strength to manage the new motion.

There are a myriad of scenarios like this, especially after injury, surgery, sedentary lifestyle, and inactivity. You will have to develop a strategy to enhance each client's ability to gain strength through a regressive to progressive approach designed to allow the neuromuscular system to adapt to the emerging mobility.

With this idea in mind, I soon devised a remedial movement pattern for this woman that caused her foot and ankle complex to load through calcaneal eversion, ankle dorsiflexion, tibial internal rotation, and forefoot abduction. This allowed her femur to rotate medially, helped flex, internally rotate, and adduct the hip, thereby loading her hip complex in three planes of motion.

This regressive movement pattern became known as the "wall banger," which is essentially a rotational squat. It is a safe and effective movement pattern we used to eccentrically load her gluteal complex in a tri-plane manner.

She immediately felt the load and was then able to control the newfound range of motion, and her gait dramatically improved.

In the physical therapy world, it has been common practice to avoid flexion, adduction, and internal rotation for those who have had hip replacement. The precaution here is directed to when doing these actions in the open chain, when the foot is not in contact with the ground and moving in open space.

However, when doing these in a closed-chain environment, the foot is firmly placed on the ground and the first metatarsal head is stabilized. The ground reaction forces and the impact of gravity pushing downward create a closed-packed environment in the hip joint, and the risk of dislocating the hip joint is greatly reduced. In my 37 years of practice, I have never observed nor heard of this happening when doing a wall banger.

Of course, as with any movement pattern, make sure the motion is coming from the Big Movement Rocks, and have the client work within the respective thresholds.

We then progressed to more advanced movements, and ultimately, she was able to return to the full activities she desired. In this case, I was able to merge her wants with her needs.

This was how my program *Flexibility Highways in Motion* was created. It is a methodology that gains integrated flexibility and matches a designated movement pattern to one of the six Flexibility Highways. It always starts with a regressive approach and progresses based on the limitations, compensations, and idiosyncrasies of each client.

For more about the program, please refer to the *Flexibility Highways in Motion DVD*, although we will also discuss more of these strategies in the chapter on program design, beginning on page 169.

## PUTTING IT ALL TOGETHER

When joints become immobile and the accompanying soft tissue becomes shortened and tight, the proprioceptors become desensitized and dysfunction can ensue. As joints become limited in motion, other structures will compensate to achieve the desired action.

Studying human motion develops a deep appreciation for the myriad of intricacies that result from the relationships of the joints and muscles. The three-dimensional interaction that occurs through the body from the ground up and from the top down has tremendous impact on optimal health and performance.

Controlled dynamic range of motion is useful in nearly all populations. The sedentary or deconditioned person will benefit from movement patterns that will gradually lengthen myofascial tissue through eccentric loading while simultaneously gaining strength.

These clients should gradually move through the patterns and increase range of motion with each repetition. With this method, we are using gravity, ground-reaction forces, bodyweight, and body angles—moving in three planes of motion—and people will be able to improve activities of daily living. These techniques are not ballistic stretches; rather, they are motions integrated into task-specific patterns.

A formula for improving effective range of motion starts with gross movement patterns, such as five to 10 minutes of low-level walking, jogging, cycling, or other activities the client enjoys and can tolerate. Follow this with tri-plane, task-specific movement patterns, starting with abbreviated motions that resemble the desired activity, and gradually increasing the range of motion. This will lengthen the tissue, sensitize the proprioceptors, and enhance a greater range of movement quality.

For the athletic population, the warm-up session should be task oriented to enhance tri-plane motions, particularly of the Big Movement Rocks of the foot and ankle complex, hips, and thoracic spine—we will discuss thesee in the next chapter.

With various movement patterns incorporating forward, backward, diagonal, lateral, and rotational movements that use lunges, jumps, and hops, a myriad of functional actions can enhance flexibility. This will not only increase range of motion, but will also prepare an athlete for sports participation while reducing the risk of injury.

After the session, add flexibility work to lengthen the soft tissue back to the resting state. Have the person hold the static stretches for 20-30 seconds and do each stretch twice. Static stretching should be multi-joint and multi-plane, using multiple muscle groups. With this approach, your client can be ready for multi-dimensional motion over a lifetime.

The excitement of studying integrated motions and the relationship of the joints to one another can provide an entirely new perspective on effective exercise programs. It is important that we use integrated flexibility programs to enhance the quality of life for all.

# CHAPTER SIX

# THE BIG MOVEMENT ROCKS— SIMPLY IMPORTANT

*"Action is the foundational key to all success."*

~ P A B L O   P I C A S S O

You will see the term "Big Movement Rocks" often in this book. These consist of the foot and ankle complex, the hips, and the thoracic spine.

Human movement is the culmination of a cascade of tri-plane motions resulting in a desired outcome whatever that may be. Efficient motion of the Big Movement Rocks improves efficiency of motion and will reduce the risk of injury.

Depending on which resources are cited, the top three injuries affecting people are low-back injury or pain, knee injury, followed by shoulder injury. My experiences over the last 37 years of practice have shown that repeated incidence of improper motion in the Big Movement Rocks significantly contributes to overuse and chronic injuries. Working closely with Dr. Robert Masson of the Neurospine Institute, I have seen many of his patients exhibit similar tendencies in movement. After evaluating their results from a gait-and-motion analysis, invariably we find tightness in the hips and thoracic spine in one or more planes of motion.

Anatomy shows us that the low back is "stuck" between the hips and thoracic spine. Chapter Two, *A Three-Dimensional Joint-by-Joint Approach to Movement* beginning on page 21, taught us that the hips are greatly affected by the foot and ankle complex and must be included within the scope of our assessments.

The knee is a victim of the foot and ankle complex and the hip. The tibia is greatly impacted by foot function and the femur is affected by hip motion, and so we see how the knee reacts to the structures above and below it. When people present with knee problems, the last place we look is the knee—we first assess the movement of the Big Movement Rocks below and above it.

The shoulder girdle involves the humerus, glenoid, clavicle, scapula, and thoracic spine. The scapula must glide over the ribs to provide proper and efficient movement of the shoulder joint. And the thoracic spine must move freely in all three planes of motion, especially in the transverse plane. If the thoracic spine has ample motion, the scapula will spontaneously glide over the ribs to allow the shoulder joint to function effectively.

However, the thoracic spine depends on freedom of motion in the hip complex, which is impacted by the foot and ankle actions. When viewing human movement, especially of a local joint, first look globally to get a perspective of gross overall tri-plane motion. Then move your assessment to the local joint action.

## THE FOOT AND ANKLE COMPLEX

Often referred to as a mobile adapter, the foot must be able to absorb forces from gravity and ground-reaction forces when moving forward and back, side to side, and in rotation. It must be able to do these actions on firm, soft, level, and unleveled surfaces, as well as on a combination.

There is a predominance of one plane of motion in certain regions of the foot, yet those regions must have a subtle action of the other two planes of motion within them.

For example, the talocrural (ankle) joint is said to be primarily a sagittal-plane mover. As the tibia moves over the talus, the motion is in the sagittal plane. However, when the foot hits the ground, contact with the ground is usually at the lateral aspect of the calcaneus.

As the ankle plantarflexes and the foot lowers to the ground, the calcaneus everts five to seven degrees, resulting in a relative rotational movement of the midfoot and forefoot as the phalanges contact the ground. At this point, the tibia starts to rotate medially, as do the femur and hip.

To envision this, imagine viewing the foot from above as seen in Figure 6.1.

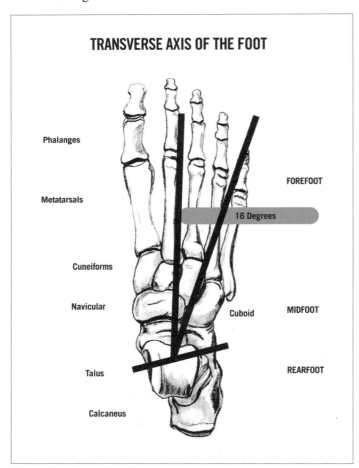

**TRANSVERSE AXIS OF THE FOOT**

Phalanges

Metatarsals

FOREFOOT

16 Degrees

Cuneiforms

Navicular

Cuboid          MIDFOOT

Talus

REARFOOT

Calcaneus

**FIGURE 6.1 TRANSVERSE AXIS OF THE FOOT**

Picture a line across the talus and have that line bisect both malleoli. Now add a line from the instep to a point between the fourth and fifth metatarsal bones. This represents an axis that passes through the talus at a 16-degree angle. This axis relates to the motion of the forefoot to the rearfoot when the foot is fully loaded in midstance.

The summation of ankle dorsiflexion in the sagittal plane, calcaneal eversion in the frontal plane, along with forefoot abduction through the transverse axis and tibia rotation in the transverse plane allows the foot and ankle complex to be loaded in three planes of motion.

For optimal foot and ankle function that will fully load the system, the following four components must occur:

- *Calcaneal eversion*
- *Tibial internal rotation*
- *Ankle dorsiflexion*
- *Forefoot abduction*

If any of these actions become limited, the entire system will be adversely affected and lack proper loading.

## THE HIP COMPLEX

The hip complex is the conduit region that conjoins the lower extremities to the torso. It must possess mobility to ambulate in three planes of motion, along with stability to assist in absorbing and transmitting forces.

The hip is comprised of the spherical femoral head and the acetabulum. Often referred to as the body's powerhouse, the hip contains the densest, most powerful muscles in the body. Thirty-three muscles attach to the hip complex; many of them exhibit the body's highest power capacity. Among them are the gluteal complex, deep hip rotators such as the piriformis, gemellae and obturator groups, adductor group, and hamstrings to name those most commonly recognized.

Like all joints in the body, the hip moves in three planes of motion. In the sagittal plane, the flexion range of motion is between 100 to 120 degrees and extension is 15 to 20 degrees.

In the frontal plane, abduction ranges from 40 to 45 degrees, while adduction is approximately 25 degrees.

In the transverse plane, internal rotation range of motion varies from 35 to 40 degrees, with external rotation of 40 to 50 degrees. In standing single-leg balance, we have observed nearly 90 degrees of external rotation.

In addition to the tri-plane range of motion, pay attention to the femoral glide that must occur for successful motion. When the hip extends, the head of the femur glides or slides forward toward the anterior. When the hip flexes, the femoral head slides posterior toward the back.

In frontal-plane motion, the femoral head slides laterally during adduction of the hip and glides medially during hip abduction.

In the transverse plane, the head of the femur rotates backward with internal rotation and rotates forward during external rotation motion.

When the hip joint gets tight, the femoral head becomes somewhat compressed in the acetabulum, resulting not only in joint compression, but also with reduced range of motion in all three planes. Therefore, when stretching the hips in three planes, you will be more successful when applying a gentle, long axis distraction, pulling the distal bone from the proximal bone.

Considering the hip structure and its important role of force transmission, the mobility of the hip is critical for successful and efficient movement patterns. People with back pain invariably have a limitation of hip function within one and most often all three planes of motion.

The close relationship of the hip complex with the lumbo-pelvic complex greatly impacts the functioning of the lumbar spine. When the hip is limited, especially in the transverse and frontal planes, the lumbar spine compensates in these planes of motion. Over time, back injury to this region follows.

In static posture, anterior pelvic tilt alignment will influence the lumbar spine by increasing lordosis. Likewise, posterior pelvic tilt causes flexion of the lumbar spine. However, the lumbar spine can also influence pelvic tilt alignment, with increased lordosis causing anterior pelvic tilt and lumbar flexion often resulting in posterior pelvic tilt.

These issues need to be correlated to your strategies of corrective exercise when developing programs. For example, if a client has an anterior pelvic tilt with increased lordosis, you need to use caution when doing squats or spinal extension movements. The rationale is that the facets of L5/S1 are closer together than in a more neutral position lumbo-pelvic complex. When squatting or moving into an extended spinal movement, the facets may compress, causing discomfort.

A lunge program is an alternative to the squat in this situation, as the hip of the forward leg will move into a posterior position while the hip of the trail leg extends. In the majority of cases, this reduces the compressive force on the L5/S1 facets. The client will be able to work the legs and hips with more comfort and efficiency.

The interesting cascade reactions of the foot have significant impact upon the hips. These principles will be discussed further throughout this book.

The hip complex is a crucial big movement rock based on the alignment and proper motion of the hips, critical function of force transmission and mitigation, and the interrelationship with the lumbar spine.

## THE THORACIC SPINE

Tri-plane motion of the thoracic spine is critical for successful and efficient movement. The span of 12 thoracic levels lends itself to be mobile in three planes of motion. The excellent book, *Low Back Disorder* by Stuart McGill, PhD, demonstrates the vast range of motion in all three planes. Cumulatively at all 12 levels, the thoracic spine averages 76 degrees in the sagittal plane of combined flexion and extension. In the frontal plane, the average range of cumulative motion is 78 degrees. In the transverse plane, the average is 74 degrees of combined left and right rotation.

Compare these ranges to the lumbar spine that totals 68 degrees of combined flexion and extension, 29 degrees of frontal plane motion, and 13 to 15 degrees in each direction of rotation.

The primary difference in the range of motion is due to the articulating facet structures of each region. The thoracic spine facets face more posterior and allow the ribs to have greater freedom of movement. The lumbar facets are aligned more obliquely and limit the movement in the transverse plane. Please refer to Figure 6.2 comparing the differences of the facet angulations between the thoracic and lumbar vertebra.

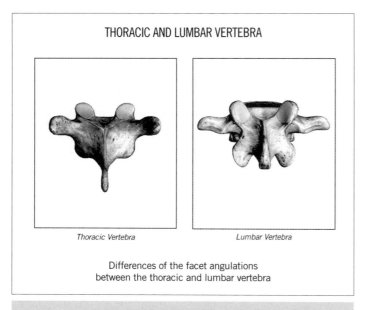

THORACIC AND LUMBAR VERTEBRA

Thoracic Vertebra

Lumbar Vertebra

Differences of the facet angulations between the thoracic and lumbar vertebra

**FIGURE 6.2 THORACIC AND LUMBAR FACET ANGULATIONS**
**PHOTO COPYRIGHT © 3D4MEDICAL**

Figure 6.3 demonstrates the difference in articulation with adjacent vertebra in each region.

The thoracic spine simultaneously functions in three planes of motion. For example, when rotating to the right, the right transverse process moves posteriorly in the sagittal plane, while the vertebral body is rotating right in the transverse plane. This is often referred to as a "coupling effect." However, in many cases there is a slight lateral flexion to the side; therefore, the frontal plane is

impacted and movement is occurring in three planes of motion.

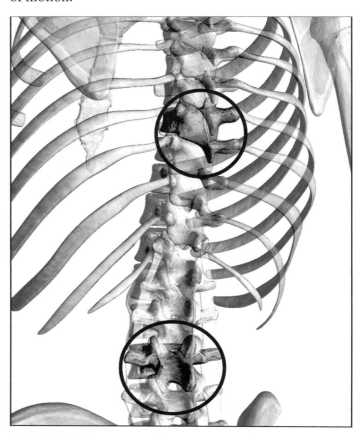

**FIGURE 6.3 VERTEBRAL ARTICULATION**
**PHOTO COPYRIGHT © 3D4MEDICAL**

There is greater motion in the upper thoracic spine from T1–T8 in the transverse plane. Farther down toward the lumbar spine, especially from T9–T12, the rotation becomes less as it approaches the thoracolumbar region. As the thoracic spine becomes more distal, the lumbar spine will influence it—it has less rotation, similar to the lumbar spine. The lumbar spine is conducive to flexion and extension, and the thoracic spine has more range of motion from T10–T12 than the level above it.

Frontal-plane motion is fairly consistent through the entire thoracic spine, as it is in the lumbar spine.

The articulation of the scapula with the thoracic spine is critical for healthy shoulder girdle and shoulder joint action. There must be good mobility in the thoracic spine to allow scapular gliding over the ribs.

This will enhance shoulder-joint mobility and create an environment for healthy shoulder movements.

## SUCCESSFUL MOVEMENT DEPENDS ON THE BIG MOVEMENT ROCKS

Throughout this book, we will continue to discuss the Big Movement Rocks and their dependency on each other for successful movement. The synergistic cascade of reactions is necessary to allow a successful environment for efficient movement. If any part of these reactions becomes limited in motion, the entire system is affected and compensatory movement patterns will contribute to complete the task.

# BLENDING TRADITION WITH FUNCTIONAL, INTEGRATED TRAINING

*"Minds are like parachutes—they only function when open."*

~ F I N L E Y  P E T E R  D U N N E

---

Before our modern transition into more integrated training methods, exercise consisted of traditional training such as Olympic lifts, selectorized equipment, and isolated training.

Using traditional methods of training is often thought of as "unlike sports." There is no question that people gain muscle mass and strength using traditional training, but there is also some limitation in movement without the addition of regular stretching. This is not a knock on isolated lifting, but at the same time, we need to be aware of those limitations.

Back in earlier days of training, the majority of strength training was done on selectorized equipment, as this was considered the "safer" alternative. In fact, the first facility I worked for implemented the gym member orientation policy to develop the initial program on weight machines due to the safety factor. How narrow-minded our field was at that time.

When I started studying human movement, I was passionate about learning how the body actually moved. I believed in this newfound concept of functional training so much that I changed my entire approach to strength and conditioning to the point that everything I did had to have a functional, integrated training aspect to it. Everything was done from a standing position; even a chest press had to be done with cables or tubing and from a standing position.

As I trained using this approach, I felt more mobile, yet less strong than I had been when using traditional lifting techniques. I had the muscle tone, but not the hypertrophy. There was more mobility, which enhanced athletics, yet sacrificed strength to some degree.

There are benefits and limitations to both methods, and even then I knew there must be a better way to gain both strength and mobility results. I kept networking with other professionals who were doing this work; I continued researching human movement, and extrapolating various training concepts to meet not only my needs and desires, but also those of my clients.

As we plan our programming, we must listen to our clients' desires, which is done through a thorough interview session with each client.

- *What is the person looking for from you?*
- *What are the goals from a physical, mental, spiritual, nutritional, and holistic health perspective?*
- *What is the client's learning style?*
- *Does the person like to be pushed with higher-intensity encouragement, or slightly nudged and gently guided through this pursuit?*

We must be good listeners when working through this process with our clients, as this is where we establish the bonds that build cohesive relationships. This time is critically important if we are to gain their trust and subsequently meet the wants of these clients.

Additionally, using a thorough health history and gait-and-motion analysis, you will take the initial steps to create the roadmap to success for your client. Based on the results gleaned from this analysis or screening, you will learn about limitations, compensations, and idiosyncrasies. For your reference, you will find the health history we use at Human Motion Associates in Appendix Five on page 223, and information about the gait analysis we use in the next chapter, beginning on page 123.

With the information obtained from this process, you will begin to understand what you will have to address to reach optimal movement, health, and wellbeing. This will help as you begin the program design process for each client.

At times, the client's wants and needs may not match. Many other times, they will merge and enhance the outcome. As you begin to understand the learning and communication style of each client, you may want to discuss how the wants and needs will mesh.

Other times, a client may not be receptive to what you know to be the needs, and you will have to subliminally blend the two, all without upsetting the client's progression. At some point during the relationship, this "wants and needs" discussion will take place at the appropriate time. This can be a critical point, when trust and communication meld together to build success in the program.

In my practice, the great majority of clients and patients are from referrals. Nearly all of them had an injury that either reoccurred or problems still lingered after numerous attempts at physical therapy or corrective strategies. Everyone I work with goes through a gait-and-motion analysis, and in most cases are found to have a limitation in one of the Big Movement Rocks of the foot and ankle complex, hips, and thoracic spine. As you know, if a limitation exists, compensation will most likely ensue.

These days, the strategies I use do not follow a typical approach to fitness, but use more of a goal-oriented Action Pyramid.

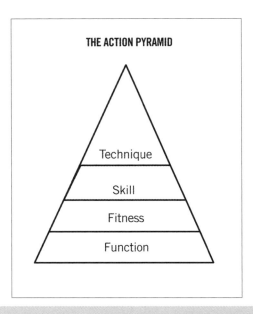

**FIGURE 7.1 THE ACTION PYRAMID**

Program design is an art based on science with the agendas centered around the client's goals, limitations, and compensations, the task objectives, and the client's needs and wants.

The Action Pyramid helps organize our thoughts into strategies directed toward a specific goal, which is derived from the assessment process. We look at the limitations, symptoms, and quality of movement, and then strive to filter results into the Action Pyramid layers.

## THE FUNCTION LAYER

Our general principle is to first determine if the foot and ankle complex, hips, and thoracic spine are too stable. In three-dimensional movements, there must be a degree of mobility to allow adequate loading in all three planes of motion. At the same time, there must be ample stability to control and decelerate the motion in three planes, stabilize the motion, and then accelerate the motion. In this sense, mobility and stability are not separate components, but are part of the same movement continuum.

Try to assess your clients using an integrated, loaded movement first, and if a limitation is revealed, cross-check it with an unweighted, open-chain, isolated-joint mobility test.

For example, if assessing the hip, have the client perform a single-leg balance with internal and external rotation to measure the degree of movement in the respective actions.

If there is a limitation, you must now determine if it is coming from the hip, foot, or ankle. This can be cross-checked in an isolated-joint mobility assessment. Compare one side to the other, as you are only concerned with how the individual client is moving, and not comparing one to others in that age group and demographic.

When the Big Movement Rocks of the foot and ankle complex, hips, and thoracic spine are too stable or immobile, the body will not be able to properly or adequately load in a tri-plane manner. This means tissue will not remodel or transmit and mitigate forces, and often this will promote compensatory movement patterns.

If this happens, the body, being a great adapter, will allow more motion in a region that normally should be stable. When mobility comes from regions that are conducive for stability, injury often follows.

When you see these conditions in a gait-and-motion analysis, you must revert back to the Action Pyramid, list the program objectives, and first work in the foundational layer—function—to gain, mobility in the foot and ankle complex, hips, and thoracic spine.

As you create an exercise plan, think in terms of the Action Pyramid, with function being the foundational layer. As you know, the bricks of the foundation are based on the information learned from your gait-and-motion analysis.

- *Where is the client limited in movement?*
- *How are the Big Movement Rocks moving in all three planes of motion?*
- *How does the client transition from the eccentric loading phase, stabilize, and then move into the concentric or unloading phase?*

If there is a temporary hesitation or the person lacks a smooth transition in some movements, this can be a sign of weakness and most often will result in a compensatory pattern.

For example, try having the client do a sagittal-plane forward lunge. Compare one side's movement against the other. Under normal, healthy conditions, the person should be able to lunge forward, decelerate the action, allow a short pause as the tissues slow the movement, then change direction and explode back to the starting position.

If after the pause or transitional phase, the person initiates the return action by driving the torso into extension, the gluteal complex on that side is probably weak. A compensatory movement pattern is occurring, with torso extension creating the momentum, rather than the action coming from the hip.

In that example, the faulty movement pattern can be due to lack of motion or strength in the foot and ankle complex or the hips and gluteal complex. Through chain-reaction biomechanics, one region may be impacting the other.

To confirm strength or mobility issues in a case where you are uncertain, you may need to do further assessment of each region to determine which complex may be lacking. If you cannot determine which is the culprit, you may need to refer your client to a physical therapist.

It is essential to gain the function of the Big Movement Rocks, if necessary, by creating a remedial or regressive movement pattern to gain optimal function of the complex.

As Gary Gray has often stated, "The test is the exercise, and the exercise is the test."

We do not always need to implement complex, nonfunctional, or nonlifelike isolated tests, but we can utilize movements the client will use in the program or in a daily activity, and work to perfect that action.

Pay particular attention to the tri-plane action of the foot and ankle complex, the hips, and the thoracic spine when doing remedial movements while improving on the foundational layer of the pyramid.

As we help our clients move better and without discomfort, in addition to the obvious musculoskeletal benefits, they gain many other physiological rewards. These include increased brain function, slowing the detriments of brain aging, increased endorphins, reduced stress and anxiety, maintenance of nerve cells, improved digestion, and better genitourinary function, just to name a few.

## THE FITNESS LAYER

Once the function base layer is established, you will move the program design to the fitness layer of the pyramid. This layer might have many objectives, such as more energy, better body composition, and preparation for a particular activity, sport, or event ranging from a power walk to a marathon.

In this phase, program design takes on different objectives as we use a hybrid approach to a periodized system, depending on the entire macro-phase or program length.

For example, say you have a client whose objective is to prepare for a sprint triathlon. If the entire program length is three months, the first three to four weeks might be spent developing muscle endurance. Assuming you plan strength training three days a week, you might start with two or three sets of 12-15 repetitions of various exercises. When the person can attain the targeted reps at the designated weights, it is time to move up in weight.

Let us assume the client started on step-ups onto a 12-inch box while holding 15-pound dumbbells for 15 reps. The program calls for ascending pyramid sets of 15 pounds for 15 reps, 20 pounds for 12 reps, and 25 pounds for 10 reps. If the client is able to perform these sets, the next session will commence at 20 pounds for 15 reps, 25 pounds for 12 reps, and 30 pounds for 10 reps.

If done with good form, yet it was stressful for the last few reps of each set, the next session will be 25 pounds for 15 reps, 30 pounds 12 reps, and 35 pounds for 10 reps, and continuing on from there.

Form is key to the execution of the movements. If or when form breaks down or the person cannot complete the designated sets, do not continue to increase the weight until the client is strong enough to handle the loads.

You will also try to match the client's cardiovascular and strength-training phases. People are usually able to capitalize efficiency without sacrificing energy when we match strength training to cardiovascular work.

When cross-matching energy systems with strength work—for example, muscle endurance work in strength programming matched with explosive modalities in cardiovascular work—the client may have more difficulty completing the program due to muscle fatigue or delayed onset muscle soreness versus when matching energy systems with strength programming.

If you change to a strength or power phase in the strength program, match the cardiovascular work with a high-intensity, short and powerful mode, such as sprints, fartleks, or high-intensity circuits. When doing explosive strength work, match the program with something like hill work and high-intensity sprint circuits. In the case of an endurance athlete such as the earlier example, work more in the frontal and transverse planes, as the majority of endurance training is sagittal-plane dominant.

Please refer to the sections further in the book for example programs, beginning on page 159.

In the foundation and fitness phases, the strategies build a base of mobility and stability through three planes of motion. The fitness phase combines the traditional methods of training with functional, integrated movement patterns.

## THE SKILL LAYER

The skill layer has a greater emphasis on multi-plane movements, sometimes with varying verticality to impact the load on the myofascial system. In this layer, ViPRs™, SandBells®, ActivMotion® Bars, Battling Ropes, weighted vests, steps of various heights, suspension trainers, and the Power Plate® are equipment examples you might recruit to provide various stimuli to the system.

As the client progresses, we modify the variables of dynamics and speed of the movement, vertical depth, reps, time, and weights. The client must be able to control the motion using bodyweight before adding external weight.

Let's say the objective is to increase the strength and mobility of the lateral gluteal complex. You might use a ViPR™ to move side to side in the frontal plane. We often start with the ViPR™ on the ground in a vertical position, with both hands holding the top, elbows extended. As the person shifts side to side, this will load the lateral gluteal complex, the same-side leg, and the opposite adductor, as seen in Photo 7.1.

**PHOTO 7.1 VIPR™ LATERAL SHIFT**

As the client moves laterally, you might add a loading stress to the latissimus dorsi by leaning the ViPR™ forward as the person moves in the frontal plane. Then have the person return to the starting position, and continue to move to the opposite side.

During this movement, watch the foot and ankle complex as it dorsiflexes in the sagittal plane—the tibia should move through internal rotation. The knee should flex, abduct, and internally rotate; the hip should move through anterior tilt, adduction, and with a slight degree of internal

rotation. Additionally, the opposite ankle complex should have a degree of relative plantar flexion because the foot is fixed to the ground. The tibia should move medially with a slight degree of internal rotation to the rearfoot, and the hips should abduct.

To progress this pattern, have the client move from the same starting position and perform a side lunge while letting the ViPR™ drop to the same side as the lunge. As the ViPR™ falls, the opposite arm reaches across and catches the ViPR™ on the way down, thereby adding an additional external vertical force as shown in photo 7.2.

**PHOTO 7.2 VIPR™ LATERAL SHUFFLE**

*This is a ViPR™ progression to gain strength in the lateral gluteal complex, as well as mobility in the adductors. Photo 7.1 shows the body decelerating forces as the ViPR™ is tilted to the right. This shifting pattern allows the left hip to adduct and recruit the lateral gluteal complex. Photo 7.2 demonstrates a more dynamic action with a lunge to the right as the left latissimus dorsi and posterior left shoulder decelerate the forces going to the right. This motion creates an internal rotation movement to load the right gluteal complex and lower extremity.*

By taking the movement from the lateral shift in the paragraph above and the lateral lunge just described, we have created a progression that loads the lateral gluteal complex and lower extremity.

Progressing up the pyramid, the skill development layer becomes more task-specific in the attempt to align the movements of the client's job, sport, or activities of daily living along with the goals of the client and the objectives of the overall program. This is the phase where creativity emerges.

Up to this point, you should be constantly evaluating the quality of movement during the exercise patterns. However, in the skill level and in the next phase of technique development, it is essential to watch for the quality of movement through the Big Movement Rocks of the foot and ankle complex, hips, and thoracic spine.

The skill and technique phases are the pillars for return to work or sport. These phases are crucial because they can develop the pathways for motor control that will eventually replicate real life where movements are more random and not under your critical-eyed supervision.

If done with care and precision, this phase, above all others, can reduce the risk of injury in activities of your client's day-to-day life.

## TECHNIQUE LAYER

The technique layer hones in on the fine motor skills necessary for high-level performance.

For example, when working with pitchers recovering from an injury, we make sure all bases are covered in the functional, fitness, and skill layers. When we get to the technique layer, we start with throwing drills before throwing any baseballs. During this phase, we may need to correct mechanics for better throwing efficiency and to reduce the risk of injury. Through these drills, we are working on hip rotation, arm slot, wrist position and action, follow-through, and timing.

When these aspects of throwing are proficient, the pitchers start throwing under our watchful eyes. The skill of throwing is a complex task and thousands of repetitions must be performed to gain proficiency. Using progressions and regressions, we try to do this as safely and as effectively as possible.

These same concepts can be applied to any sport or work-related activity. Prior to commencing work in the skill or techniques layers, study the desired action in detail for return to play or return to work. This study will enhance your creativity and your client's overall outcome.

When working with clients who have had an injury or surgery, it is important to progress them through the phases of the Action Pyramid. Many clients who have passed through the function and fitness layers become frustrated after a physician or physical therapist has cleared them to return to work or play, because even though they obtained medical clearance, they may not be ready for higher-level activities.

For example, professional athletes may receive medical clearance, however they are often sent to lower levels of play to work on the skill and technique layers to prepare for competition at a higher level.

Likewise, people who work in intense physical jobs such as construction, warehouse, or factory environments also need to prepare for the rigors of those complex and intense jobs. When people go through the technical and skill phases, they are more fit to the demands at hand.

## PUTTING IT ALL TOGETHER

Using the Action Pyramid model helps me follow a consistent thought process to develop strategies and programs for a variety of issues clients present. Using this model and coupling it with the 4Q Model found in Chapter 10 on page 166 will help you to visualize the plan, enhance movement variability and creativity, and assist in keeping clients motivated, all to help meet their goals and improve their movement efficiency.

# CHAPTER EIGHT

# THE FUNCTIONAL ASSESSMENT

*"Look deep into nature, and then you will
understand everything better."*

~ ALBERT EINSTEIN

---

Throughout this book, I tell you to do some type of movement assessment or screen prior to programming each client. It does not matter which type of screening you do; it matters that you do it consistently so that over time you will understand what you are seeing in each client's results.

Gary Gray and the Gray Institute first taught me the foundation of the methods we use now for gait-and-motion analysis. Gary has done a magnificent job in bringing chain-reaction biomechanics and movement-assessment techniques to the forefront of our field.

In another screening example, Gray Cook and Lee Burton pioneered the Functional Movement Screen (FMS) and have done great work in organizing a systematic process to bring awareness of the movements of clients and providing a ranking system to their movement patterns. Many people are successful using the FMS screening system.

At Human Motion Associates, we use the Gray Institute approach as the foundation—I highly recommend the programs from the Gray Institute. To that work, we have added techniques to observe movement by many of the great pioneers in gait analysis such as Verne Inman, Daniel Elfman, Daria Dykyj, Sven Carlsoo, and Merton Root.

Additionally, having the opportunity to work with Drs. Robert Masson, Michael Ray, Randy Schwartzberg, Daryl Osbahr, and Amit Varma has allowed me to observe their medical evaluations and blend those into our program to help unravel the complexities of movement of our clients and patients.

When performing a gait-and-motion analysis, try to obtain an objective view of the clients, what their limitations and compensations may be, and understand their goals whether those are fitness, health, or activities of daily living.

We do not use the normative data for range of motion of a particular joint for a given demographic, gender, size, or age of the person. Instead, compare the person to the person or, as Gary Gray has stated, compare *you to you*.

After performing a gait-and-motion analysis, the criteria to use to measure the change in range of motion (hopefully for the better) should be based on quality of movement. Redo the analysis periodically to see if any previous compensations have been reduced or completely removed.

In the majority of cases, we use a very powerful app called *Spark Motion,* which is available from the Apple Store. I highly recommend it or any other motion capture app you find easily useable.

When doing a gait-and-motion analysis, break the assessment into two aspects, the gait portion to evaluate how a person is walking as compared to the expected outcomes of a "normal" gait. The other aspect we use is a motion analysis utilizing the Total Gym® Functional Movement Grid.

The following are instructions on the tests we most often use at Human Motion Associates, although there are many others we might use based on the issues a client presents. These techniques have been successful in our clinic.

However, there are other tools you can use with great success in your gait-and-motion analysis.

The order of using these evaluation tools is the approach with which I have become comfortable. Feel free to change the order or to use other techniques you may be comfortable using. This is not the only way to assess. The goal here is to share information that has been useful in our facilities.

## GAIT ANALYSIS

The first thing to do is have people walk normally. At first, they may appear stiff, hesitant, or rigid as they are not used to having their walking motion critically viewed. Remind them to relax.

I prefer to first watch them as they walk away from me. This gives a better perspective to view from the posterior side. Start watching the hip motion to assess how each hip extends in the sagittal plane. Look for the symmetry of one side versus the other. In other words, do the hips extend equally or is there a difference from one to the other?

Simultaneously, watch for frontal-plane motion through hip adduction and compare one side to the other. Does one hip adduct more than the other? Is there any hip adduction at all?

From the hips, you would then watch the foot function. Do the feet pronate, overpronate, or supinate? Is the client able to get the first metatarsal head to stabilize on the ground? Does the heel of either foot move medially into a heel whip?

After getting an idea of the feet, move up to observe the thoracic spine. Does it rotate equally to the right and left? Does it rotate more to one side as compared to the other? Does the thoracic spine rotate appreciably or does the person walk like Frankenstein?

After viewing from behind, have the client walk back toward you. Now you can observe the same motions as from the posterior side, but this view allows us to see the hips move into the transverse plane.

Do this by watching the midline to see if it rotates equally to each side or more to one side. Also, watch the crease of the clothing at the hip to see if there is more of a crease on one side versus the other. If there is more of a crease on one side, correlate that with the rotation of the midline and try to determine if there is more transverse plane motion on one side as compared to the other.

Look at hip adduction on one side along with hip abduction on the other side to see if those motions are symmetrical.

Lastly, watch the arm swing to see if they move equally, especially the scapular motion from the posterior side.

What you often will find is when there is limited motion in the hip or thoracic spine in the transverse plane, the person will not load in the frontal plane as efficiently and vice versa.

You can then view the gait pattern from the side to see if stride length is symmetrical.

After reviewing that commentary, practice watching the gait of friends or family. It will not take you long to begin to notice quality and discrepancies in gait, and soon you will become confident in using gait analysis with your clients.

## MOTION ANALYSIS

As we complete the gait analysis, we move immediately into a motion analysis using some or all of the following assessments.

### WALKING WITH BILATERAL ARM REACH IN THE TRANSVERSE PLANE

In this assessment, tell the clients to imagine they are holding a basketball. As they walk, they reach both arms at shoulder height into the lead leg and repeat to the opposite side. This means with the left leg forward, reach to the left; when the right leg is forward, reach to the right.

Through this test, look at thoracic rotation to either side. Additionally, view hip motion to see if the thoracic motion is influencing the hip motion into internal hip rotation. Compare one side to the other from both the anterior and posterior views.

PHOTO 8.1 WALKING WITH BILATERAL ARM
REACH IN THE TRANSVERSE PLANE

## WALKING WITH OVERHEAD BILATERAL ARM REACH TO THE OPPOSITE SIDE

This test is to determine the range of motion of the hips in the frontal plane. Tell the client to stand tall with both arms overhead. As the client steps with the left leg, have the person reach both hands and arms overhead and to the right. Repeat the opposite actions when stepping right while reaching to the left.

In cases where people are tight in the lateral gluteal complex, they may not have the ability to adduct the hips. Even though one of the primary objectives of assessment is to see how the client subconsciously moves, when the hips are tight in the frontal plane, ask them to drive their hips side to side when walking. This will give you a better idea if there is available motion in the frontal plane.

A common compensation pattern we often see when clients are tight in the lateral gluteal complex is the foot of the tight hip will turn inward. This occurs as a result of weakness in the hip where the inward rotation lengthens the gluteal complex in the transverse plane to provide

more stability. This will often be verified with other tests that assess the strength and mobility in the frontal plane.

When doing this assessment, compare one side to the other. Remember, if the client is tight and weak into hip adduction, you will see limited internal rotation in that hip. This test not only investigates hip adduction, but also looks at hip abduction of the opposite hip as well. The inability to adduct a hip may indicate tightness on that side, or could be a lack of motion in abduction on the opposite side.

PHOTO 8.2 WALKING WITH OVERHEAD BILATERAL
ARM REACH TO THE OPPOSITE SIDE

## LONG STRIDE AND FAST WALK

When people walk with a fast gait, their gait tendencies often become more exaggerated. With a long stride, those tendencies really become evident. When walking both fast *and* with long strides, the compensations become very apparent.

As you see this, watch from the anterior and posterior views, as well as the lateral aspect. This way, you will see motion of the Big Movement Rocks from the sagittal and transverse planes when viewed from the anterior and posterior aspects. The lateral view will allow you to evaluate stride-length symmetry, as well as forward and back oscillation of the torso during each stride of the cycle, including any upward oscillation.

### SINGLE-LEG MINI-SQUAT

Have the client stand on one foot with the non-weight–bearing foot next to and slightly behind the stance leg. We use this position because when behind the stance leg, it allows the hip of the weight-bearing leg to move into a slight anterior tilt during the initial phase of the mini-squat. If the client cannot maintain balance, you can instead suggest a minimal toe touch, allowing the non-weight–bearing foot to help with balance.

Have the client do a squat to about one-third of the full range of motion. In this small movement, the foot and ankle complex must go through the four components of foot-and-ankle function of calcaneal eversion, tibial internal rotation, ankle dorsiflexion, and forefoot abduction.

Additionally, view the client's ability to maintain good balance, and check to see if the first metatarsal head can stabilize against the ground. When people cannot stabilize the first ray to the ground, often the four lesser toes flex or "claw" to attempt to maintain balance and stability. If the first ray stabilizes on the ground, this usually does not happen as prominently.

View this motion from the front view and side views. The front view allows you to see if the forefoot is abducting, if the tibia moves into internal rotation, and if first ray stabilizes to the ground. Ankle dorsiflexion is better viewed from the lateral aspect.

Lastly, check ankle dorsiflexion in an isolated, open-chain test. However, when doing this you are only looking at the talocrural joint in the sagittal plane. This does not take into account the other three components of successful integrated ankle-and-foot actions of tibial internal rotation, forefoot abduction, and calcaneal eversion. If any one of these actions is limited in motion, the entire reaction will be compensated.

**PHOTO 8.3 SINGLE-LEG MINI-SQUAT, LATERAL VIEW**

**PHOTO 8.4 SINGLE-LEG MINI-SQUAT, FRONT VIEW**

After completing those simple assessments, we move on to an unweighted foot assessment.

# THE FOOT ASSESSMENT

### THE SUBTALAR JOINT

We do the foot assessment in an unweighted position. Have the client sit on a table with the feet hanging downward. With the leg relaxed, place the right calcaneus in the palm of your left hand. Rest the foot on your left forearm with the ankle in a neutral position.

Place your right hand at the lower tibia two or three inches above the ankle as shown in Photo 8.5.

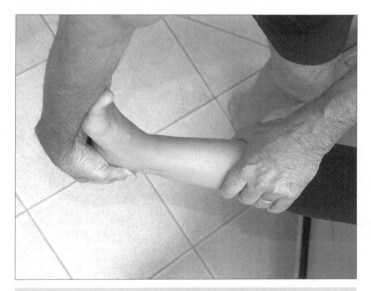

**PHOTO 8.5 SUBTALAR JOINT, NEUTRAL POSITION**

Simultaneously, turn the calcaneus outward into eversion while turning the tibia inward into internal rotation to allow the subtalar joint to evert. Then reverse the motion by turning the calcaneus inward (inversion) and the tibia outward (external rotation) to allow the subtalar joint to invert as shown in Photos 8.6 and 8.7.

Under normal, healthy conditions, there should be approximately six to 12 degrees of motion. Compare one side to the opposite side.

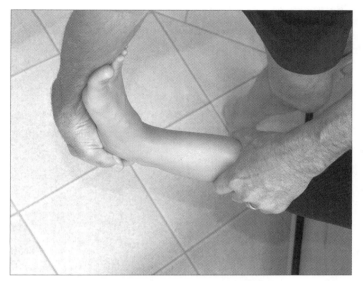

**PHOTO 8.6 SUBTALAR JOINT EVERSION—HERE THE RIGHT HAND TURNS THE CALCANEUS LATERALLY, WHILE THE LEFT HAND ROTATES MEDIALLY**

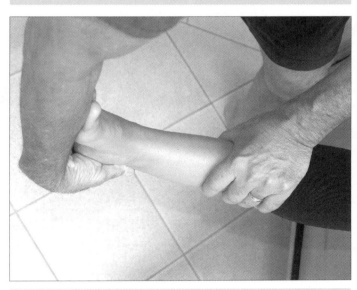

**PHOTO 8.7 SUBTALAR JOINT INVERSION—NOW THE RIGHT HAND TURNS THE CALCANEUS MEDIALLY, WHILE THE LEFT HAND ROTATES LATERALLY**

## THE METATARSAL JOINTS

Have the client sit on a table with the feet hanging down-ward. With the leg relaxed, hold the right midfoot with your left hand, while holding the metatarsal bones with your right hand.

Move the right hand upward toward the head—ceph-alad—and downward toward the distal spine—caudal. There should be approximately 10 degrees of motion. Please refer to Photos 8.8–8.10.

Compare one side with the other.

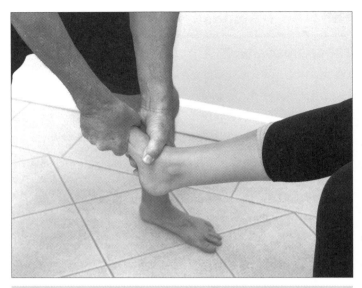

**PHOTO 8.9 METATARSAL JOINT DORSIFLEXED**

*The left hand holds the foot distal to the ankle, while the right hand mobilizes at the metatarsophalangeal joint cephalad or toward the head.*

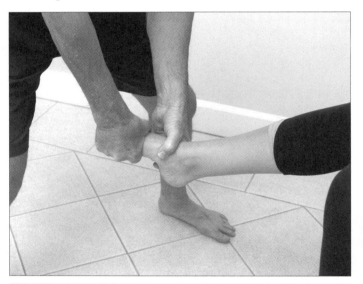

**PHOTO 8.8 METATARSAL JOINT START POSITION**

*The left hand holds the foot distal to the ankle, while the right hand holds at the metatarsophalangeal joint.*

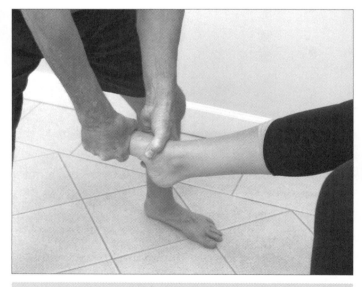

**PHOTO 8.10 METATARSAL JOINT PLANTARFLEXED**

*The left hand holds the foot distal to the ankle, while the right hand mobilizes at the metatarsophalangeal joint caudally into plantar flexion.*

### THE GREAT TOE

While holding the foot with one hand, move the great toe into dorsiflexion. There should be anywhere from 35 to 45 degrees of movement. Please see Photo 8.11.

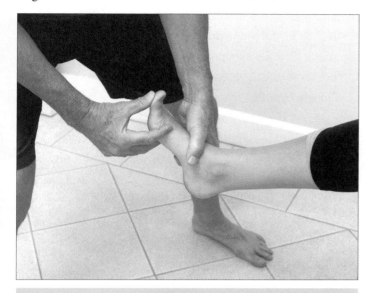

**PHOTO 8.11 THE GREAT TOE, DORSIFLEXED**

*The left hand holds the midfoot, while the right hand dorsiflexes the great toe.*

There may be a scope of practice question here for those who work in facilities that limit hands-on approaches beyond assisted stretching. These techniques do not adjust or manipulate joints, but rather assess motion. Additionally, no diagnosis is made from these techniques—just extrapolation on the limitations that may occur considering the principles of biomechanics. Check the policy and philosophy of your facility before using these foot assessment techniques.

At the completion of the foot assessment, we use a Total Gym® Functional Testing Grid for further evaluation.

# THE FUNCTIONAL TESTING GRID

The Total Gym® Functional Testing Grid balance reach excursion test allows us to look at an integrated chain reaction. This shows how a client moves through certain actions in each plane of motion.

When doing these tests, assess how the client is able to maintain balance, decelerate, stabilize, and accelerate through the actions of each test. Look for compensatory patterns.

The last measurement we do is to look at how far the client reaches. We are more concerned with the quality and not the quantity of movement.

Remember to compare the clients to themselves, particularly one side to the other, and not to the normative data for their age, gender, or size.

The testing grid is divided into 12 30-degree segments from zero to 360 degrees. This can also be divided into right and left halves such as zero to 180 to the right, and zero to 180 to the left. Have the client face forward to the zero-degree aspect and test from that position.

### SINGLE-LEG BALANCE ANTERIOR REACH TO ZERO DEGREES—SAGITTAL PLANE

This test measures the loading capability of the foot, ankle, and hip in an integrated manner in the sagittal plane. Have the client stand barefoot with the great toe of the left foot on the center dot where all the vectors intersect. Make sure the medial border of the foot is parallel and on the line of the north-to-south vector.

Tell the client to reach with the right foot as far as possible along the north-to-south vertical vector. Allow the ankle to dorsiflex and the knee to flex as well. View Photo 8.12 to get an idea of how to execute this test. View this from the front to see all the actions necessary for success and from the lateral side to watch ankle dorsiflexion.

**PHOTO 8.12 SINGLE-LEG BALANCE ANTERIOR REACH TO ZERO DEGREES—SAGITTAL PLANE**

### SINGLE-LEG BALANCE LATERAL REACH TO 90 DEGREES—FRONTAL PLANE

This test measures the loading capability of the foot, ankle, and hip in an integrated manner in the frontal plane. Have the client stand barefoot with the great toe of the left foot on the center dot where all the vectors intersect. Make sure the medial border of the foot is parallel and on the line of the north-to-south vector.

Tell the client to reach with the right foot as far as possible along the east-to-west 90-degree vector. They are allowed to ankle dorsiflex and flex the knee as well. View Photo 8.13 to see how to execute this test. Watch this from the front to view all the actions necessary for success and use the lateral view to see ankle dorsiflexion.

The actions to watch for are calcaneal eversion, ankle dorsiflexion, tibial internal rotation, and forefoot abduction. You also want to look for balance and fluidity of motion that takes into account the ability to decelerate the motion and accelerate back to the starting position.

Additionally, watch to see the movement of the knee, as it should abduct and internally rotate into a valgus position. Excessive knee valgus and the inability to control and move back into the starting position is very important to assess. Remember, the knee is the dumbest joint in the body and will do what the foot and hip tell it to do. In this test, the foot has particular influence on knee function.

The last point to consider is the length of the person's reach, as this only serves as a reference point. However, when reassessing, you can use it to measure and check for changes from earlier tests.

**PHOTO 8.13 SINGLE-LEG BALANCE LATERAL REACH TO 90 DEGREES—FRONTAL PLANE**

The actions to watch for are calcaneal eversion, ankle dorsiflexion, tibial internal rotation, and forefoot abduction. Also, look for balance and fluidity of motion that additionally takes into account the ability to decelerate the motion and accelerate back to the starting position.

Again, the last point to consider is the length of reach as this only serves as a reference point to use when reassessing.

When performing a lateral reach test, the movement of the lateral reach of the opposite extremity will cause the balance foot to evert more. The weight-bearing knee will move into valgus farther. Not only will this test the foot function in the frontal plane, but it will also challenge the weight-bearing hip to control frontal and transverse plane action of the lower extremity. If the hip is weak, the knee will go into a valgus movement for a longer period of time, as well as into greater knee valgus or abduction.

If the foot of the weight-bearing side is weak or has a rearfoot control problem, the knee will also be affected. Check to see how the client controls the action and then returns to the start position.

### SINGLE-LEG BALANCE INTERNAL AND EXTERNAL ROTATION—TRANSVERSE PLANE

Next, have the client stand barefoot in the center of the grid with the calcaneus on the center dot with the hands on the hips and the hip directly over the foot. The client will place nearly full weight over the balancing foot while the non-weight–bearing foot lightly touches the ground to balance. Have the client place the hands on the hips. As the person moves, make sure the shoulders and hips move together. Do not let the shoulders move separately from the hips during the rotation moment.

The client will face forward to the zero-degree mark. Use the midline of the body as the reference point to measure the distance the person moves. Have the person move into external rotation in a steady motion—to the right if measuring the left hip, to the left if measuring the right hip. Make note of the body's midline to the range of motion

traveled on the grid. Mark when the client either stops and cannot go farther, or hesitates and then continues moving through external rotation.

Following the endpoint of external rotation, the client will then start moving into internal rotation and continue as far as possible past the zero-degree mark. As the client moves farther into internal rotation, it is important to keep the balance foot firmly on the ground, not inverting the foot. The mark of the range of motion is when the person either hesitates and then continues through internal rotation, cannot go farther, or lifts the weight-bearing foot into inversion.

The reference point of measurement is the midline of the pelvis or the umbilicus.

**PHOTO 8.14 SINGLE-LEG BALANCE EXTERNAL ROTATION**

**PHOTO 8.15 SINGLE-LEG BALANCE INTERNAL ROTATION**

### ANTERIOR OR POSTERIOR PELVIC TILT

This test is to determine if there is a difference in pelvic tilt sagittal plane motion. Tell the client to stand tall with both arms overhead while balancing on one leg. You will stand on one side and hold the client's wrist. Your other hand should be placed on the client's iliac crest so you can feel the motion of the hip as it extends and flexes when the client rocks back and forth within a 10-degree range.

Have the client rock forward and back while maintaining the stand-tall posture. As the person rocks back and reaches with both hands into a posterior overhead reach, the non-weight–bearing foot and leg should reach forward.

The client then reverses the motion and reaches to an anterior overhead reach, while the non-weight-bearing foot and leg move backward. When the client reaches posterior overhead, it causes the hip on the weight-bearing side to move into anterior tilt, while reaching anterior overhead will cause the hip to move into posterior tilt.

Your lower hand will feel the anterior and posterior motion of the hip so you can compare one side to the other. Regarding range of motion, the results will be equal or within normal limits (WNL) or left greater than right (L>R) or right greater than left (R>L).

**PHOTO 8.16 ANTERIOR TILT TEST**

**PHOTO 8.17 POSTERIOR TILT TEST**

## THORACIC SPINE ROTATION

The thoracic spine rotation test determines range of motion of the thoracic spine in the transverse plane. The client stands in the middle of the grid over the center of the intersection of all vectors. Have the person stand with the feet comfortably at hip-width apart.

To assess right rotation, put your right hand on the right sacroiliac joint and the left hand on the left anterior superior iliac crest. To assess left rotation, place your left hand on the left sacroiliac joint and the right hand on the right anterior superior iliac crest.

Have the client place the arms across the chest, with the eyes fixated forward. As you stand closely behind the person, peer over the client's shoulder and watch the degrees of rotational range of motion in the torso. Change the hand positions and repeat to view the left rotation. Repeat the same test, but allow the client to turn the head in the same direction during the rotation.

Another way to note rotation is to observe how much the shoulders turn and line that with the degrees of rotation on the grid. For example, in Photo 8.18 the shoulders are rotated right approximately 45 degrees. The shoulders are aligned with the markings on the grid that measure about 45 degrees from the start position.

The reason to do this with the eyes fixated and then turning the head is to assess if there is tightness in the cervical spine that may inhibit thoracic spine motion.

**PHOTO 8.18 THORACIC SPINE ROTATION TO THE RIGHT**

## FRONTAL PLANE LUNGE—
## TESTS FOR ADDUCTOR AND LATERAL
## GLUTEAL TIGHTNESS AND STABILITY

Have the client stand facing forward with the right fifth phalange—the fifth toe—on the 90-degree line of the Total Gym® Functional Testing Grid. The client will perform a frontal-plane side lunge to the left.

Any distance to the left of the midline on the grid is referred to as a positive range of motion—for example, plus 45 degrees. If unable to reach beyond the left of the midline, this is a negative range of motion, such as minus 10 degrees.

Repeat from the left side with the left fifth phalange on the left 90-degree mark, then lunging to the right. If unable to reach the right of the midline, this is a negative range of motion.

Mark the range of motion. Additionally, make note of the quality of movement of the trail leg.

Watch to see if the trail knee is flexed and internally rotated. If there is knee flexion and femoral internal rotation, the adductor on that side is tight.

Compare the difference in each adductor in Photos 8.19 and 8.20. Photo 8.20 demonstrates a tighter adductor as the right knee is slightly flexed and the femur is rotated inward.

**PHOTO 8.20 FRONTAL PLANE LUNGE TO THE LEFT—OBSERVE THE TIGHT RIGHT ADDUCTOR AND THE FLEXED AND INTERNALLY ROTATED RIGHT KNEE**

**PHOTO 8.19 FRONTAL PLANE LUNGE TO THE RIGHT—OBSERVE THE LEFT ADDUCTOR AND THE EXTENDED KNEE**

### SCAPULAR MOTION

Place your hand on the inferior angle of the client's scapula. Have the client move the shoulder into shoulder flexion, shoulder abduction, and horizontal flexion, and then into horizontal extension with internal and external rotation.

Palpate the motion of the scapula to feel the range of motion, tightness, and speed of motion of one scapula as compared to the other. Make a note if there is a difference of one scapula being tighter or moving slower than the other, and in which plane of motion you felt the difference.

## REVIEW OF THESE ASSESSMENTS

There are many other assessment techniques we use if we want to further verify the quality of motion in a particular region. The techniques demonstrated above are the foundational patterns we use.

We need to understand how our clients move and investigate why they move as they do to develop roadmaps of each client's movement patterns. I am not abdicating that this is the only approach to implement. If you have other systems you prefer to apply, please do so.

As you unravel movement complexities, you will be able to create a truly personalized exercise and movement prescription based upon client idiosyncrasies, limitations, and compensations.

This can be a complex approach to understanding the issues that face each client. You must practice these techniques—or any other you choose—to become proficient and ultimately to assist people toward improved wellbeing. When you can do this, you will open up avenues to help your clients as well as increase referrals and revenue.

# PREPROGRAMMING INSIGHTS

*"Form follows function."*

~ S E R G E  G R A C O V E T S K Y

---

Through all these years in practice, "aha" moments often helped unravel the complexities clients presented, many anecdotal with no scientific research or peer-reviewed study behind them. As necessary as research and peer reviews are, there are times when repetition and intuition can serve as powerful reinforcement.

When we are able to reproduce these experiences with the same or nearly the same results, there is something to be said about the position or perspective. Sometimes we get lucky. Sometimes, when luck hits more than once with similar results, that is an "aha" moment.

In this chapter, you will read the rationale for why these were eye-opening experiences, as well as the biomechanical reasoning behind them. These insights are organized into the following sections:

- *Biomechanical Issues*
- *Cueing*
- *Industry Observations*

These are not diagnoses, nor are they substitutes for the need to refer to a medical professional when appropriate. You should not use these in your program design without doing a gait-and-motion analysis or similar movement screening. However, it is important to be aware of these issues before designing your programs.

## BIOMECHANICAL ISSUES

Eighty-four percent of people employing personal trainers have a chronic injury, according to the *2013 International Dance and Exercise Association (IDEA) Personal Training and Equipment Trends* study by Jan Schroeder, PhD and Shawn Dolan, PhD. Additionally, 25% of the clientele are between the ages of 55-64 years of age; 33% are between 45-54 years old, and 21% are 65 or older.

These baby boomers are nearing retirement years and have developed lifestyle-related biomechanical issues that plague their quality of life. Understanding the biomechanical factors of movement can address many of the problems they face, and a corrective exercise strategy may have a positive impact upon their wellbeing.

### THE BIG MOVEMENT ROCKS

» **INSIGHT:** The three most common overuse injury issues are the low back, the knee, and the shoulder. Each of these is "stuck" between the foot and ankle complex, the hips, and the thoracic spine. When any of these Big Movement Rocks become limited in motion, overuse often ensues at one of those three common injury sites.

Back pain is the number-one injury worldwide. In 2015, more than $216 billion globally was attributed to costs stemming from low-back pain, and it is the second-most common reason for physician office visits. In the United States, low-back pain accounts for $90 billion in healthcare costs each year.

Referring back to our concepts of movement, the low back is "stuck" between the hips and the thoracic spine, the two most mobile regions of the body. If either region is limited in motion, the risk of lumbar injury increases.

This is particularly true if motion in the hips and thoracic spine is tight in the transverse plane. It is critical to maintain mobility in the hips and t-spine in all three planes of motion. Remember, if there is tightness in these Big Movement Rocks, look globally to see how the feet are functioning as well.

Similarly, the knee is between the foot and ankle complex and the hips. If there is a dysfunction in either region, the knee often compensates during movement patterns.

» **INSIGHT: Most people presenting with low-back pain have a motion limitation in the foot and ankle complex, the hips, and thoracic spine. Make sure these Big Movement Rocks have good range of motion to reduce compensations in the lumbar region.**

Review the gait reaction cycle, as seen in Photos 9.1 A, B, C, and D.

*Notice the extended hip and the thoracic spine rotation to the right. The right hip is higher than the left during the mid-stance phase.*

View the right hip hike in Photo 9.1A, while the thoracic spine is rotating to the right and the left hip is extended. The right hip is slightly higher to allow room for the left swing leg. The thoracic spine is rotated right, while the left hip is extended.

In Photos 9.1C and D, the opposite reaction occurs.

**PHOTOS 9.1 C AND D GAIT STRIDE WITH LEFT FOOT FORWARD**

*Notice the extended right hip and the thoracic spine rotation to the left. The left hip is higher than the right during the mid-stance phase.*

**PHOTOS 9.1 A AND B: GAIT STRIDE**

**PHOTOS 9.1 E AND F LATERAL VIEW**

*Review the posterior tilt of the left hip in Photo 9.1E in relation to the anterior tilt of the left extended hip in Photo 9.1F.*

During the gait cycle, as the hip extends, it will normally tilt forward or anteriorly. Simultaneously, the opposite arm will swing forward, causing the thoracic spine to rotate toward the opposite side. This series of actions allows successful reactions in the lumbar spine to load in all three planes of motion and provide the "clearance" of the facets and transverse processes, and reduces excessive "jamming" that can lead to degeneration.

If foot or ankle actions are compromised, the tibia will not internally rotate, the knee will not load in three planes—flexion, abduction, and internal rotation—and the hip will not load in three planes—flexion, adduction, and internal rotation.

This often leads to a reduction of transverse-plane motion and a predominance of sagittal-plane movement. This causes excessive frontal-plane motion to allow for the leg to move forward during the swing phase of gait. If this occurs for long periods of time, the facets in the lumbar spine are exposed to abnormal articulation that can lead to degeneration.

Additionally, the soft tissue of the multifidus, intertransversarii, and the tissue between the vertebral processes shorten, as they are not eccentrically loaded in the transverse plane. Over time, this can lead to joint compression and, quite likely, to degeneration.

### THE HIP

» **INSIGHT: When a client presents with kyphosis, we have historically addressed the thoracic spine. However, there is a chain reaction following scapular protraction. The thoracic and lumbar spine flexes, lordosis is lost, and the pelvis most often will go into posterior tilt. Is kyphosis a thoracic or pelvic problem? Both need to be involved in the solution.**

For decades, physical therapists and fitness professionals have addressed kyphotic posture by stretching the anterior musculature of the shoulder complex and strengthening the posterior aspect.

This only focuses on part of the problem—let's also look at pelvic alignment. In the majority of cases, when a person presents with rounded shoulders, the pelvis is in a posterior-tilted position.

To demonstrate, stand with one hand on a hip and the other on your lumbar spine. Become kyphotic, and notice as the hip tilts posteriorly, the lumbar and thoracic spine regions flex, the shoulders protract, the cervical spine flexes, and the head shifts forward and down.

Now place your left foot forward into a long staggered stance. Drive your left knee over your shoelaces. Observe how your right hip is now extended and the hip is anteriorly tilted, which extends the lumbar spine, resulting in a relative lordotic posture.

Stand tall from your greater trochanter of the hip to the top of your head. Observe the extension of your thoracic spine, the retraction of your shoulders, and the increased cervical lordosis.

Next, reach your left hand forward and flex at the hip. This loads the Posterior Flexibility Highway described on page 99. Extend back to the upright position while reaching your left hand past your left hip and into shoulder extension as viewed in Photo 9.2. While doing this, rotate your pelvis toward the left leg. This allows you to recapture your posture alignment, while at the same time stretching the left shoulder and pectoral region. This stretches the Anterior X-Factor (see page 103) from the right hip flexor up to the left shoulder.

**PHOTO 9.2 LEFT LEG FORWARD WITH SAME-SIDE ARM EXTENSION**

Concomitantly, this movement pattern strengthens the left posterior shoulder, while lengthening the left gluteal complex and the right latissimus dorsi along the Posterior X-Factor as explained on page 104.

To functionally improve the cervical spine, the lumbar spine must be relatively extended so lordosis is gained in this region, which will allow the thoracic spine to gain extension. This creates an environment for the cervical spine to be in a lordotic position to allow for proper motion.

> » **INSIGHT:** When a client has limited internal rotation of the hip, one of the issues you need to assess is the motion of the hip in the frontal plane. If a person cannot adduct the hip, the transverse plane of internal rotation will be affected. This should be assessed from a closed-chain upright position, as well as in an open-chain motion.

The biomechanical reaction from the ground up provides the perspective for this idea. In a normal, healthy gait, as the foot hits the ground, the calcaneus everts, the tibia internally rotates, the ankle dorsiflexes, and the forefoot abducts.

With tibial internal rotation, the knee flexes in the sagittal plane, abducts in the frontal plane, and internally rotates in the transverse plane. The femur follows into medial rotation, while the hip adducts in the frontal plane and flexes in the sagittal plane. If any one of these motions becomes limited, the entire kinetic chain compensates.

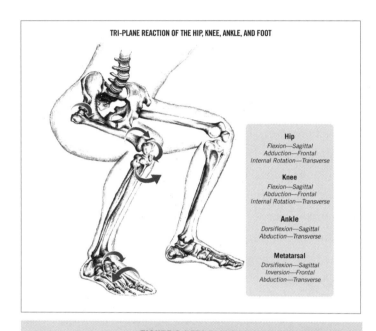

**FIGURE 9.1 TRI-PLANE LOADING CHAIN REACTION**

When focusing on the hip, the frontal and transverse planes are dependent upon each other for a successful action in either plane of motion. Many common tendencies with compensated gait emerge in people who have had hip, knee, or ankle injury or surgery. With any of these myofascial injuries, if a person cannot load into mid-stance weight bearing, the hip will not adduct to its capability and transverse-plane action of internal rotation is limited.

For example, nearly everyone who has had hip surgery or hip replacement has difficulty loading into internal hip rotation. Likewise, this population has limited hip adduction. When these clients attempt to get into internal hip rotation, they will be limited in the pursuit.

The initial reaction is to stop forcing them into rotation, primarily because they are uncomfortable. Instead, work in a different plane of motion. Using a strategy to mobilize the frontal plane will be more successful; the clients feel better, and you can begin to work through the transverse plane. You will be making headway to improved gait patterns with less discomfort.

Try this for yourself—stand on your left foot in an abducted position by placing your foot outside your hip as in Photo 9.3.

**PHOTO 9.3 HIP ABDUCTION WITH INTERNAL ROTATION**

*Stand with an abducted hip. If the external hip rotators are tight, internal rotation into that hip will be reduced.*

Now, toe touch with your non-weight–bearing foot and turn into the abducted hip. Mark your motion from the start to end positions.

Now return to the starting position, adduct your hip by moving your hip outside or lateral to your foot and repeat the same action—see Photo 9.4.

**PHOTO 9.4 HIP ADDUCTION WITH INTERNAL ROTATION**

*Stand with an adducted hip. If the external hip rotators have good range of motion, internal rotation into that hip will be enhanced.*

Most people have greater range of motion when the hip is adducted. Many also feel less pressure in the lumbosacral region of the low back.

Be aware of this tri-plane relationship, not only for the issues discussed, but also for the sedentary or elderly with limited motion in the frontal plane during the gait cycle. Even in cases when no injury has occurred, this becomes apparent in those lacking ankle dorsiflexion. If ankle dorsiflexion is limited, we become sagittal-plane dominant and compensate gait in the frontal plane. When this occurs, the transverse plane is also negatively impacted.

» **INSIGHT:** As the right leg swings through on a fixed left foot on the ground, the right leg turns the pelvis into the left hip on the fixed femur. According to the principle of the distal bone in relation to the proximal bone, the left hip moves into internal rotation prior to heel-off.

In motion, the ankle joint moves primarily in the sagittal plane. It needs some degree of frontal-plane action, but not to the point that it creates too much mobility, which increases the risk of ankle injuries. This concept is important, as it is critical for the foot and ankle to undergo these actions to create an environment for successful knee and hip function.

» **INSIGHT: If the hip appears to "bail out" during mid-stance of a client's gait cycle, take a look at the adductors and the foot. Often the adductors are tight in the transverse plane. The foot may have problems stabilizing the first ray during mid-stance.**

This scenario can be confusing, but with critical thought you can resolve it. It is most beneficial to assess this reaction from the posterior view because you can see what is happening through the foot actions and see the impact on the lower extremity and hip.

These cases are typically a result of a forefoot abductovarus, where the forefoot is abducted to the rearfoot. If you view the foot straight on and in a non-weight-bearing mode, you will notice the great toe is higher off the ground than the fifth toe. The toes run on an angle with the great toe higher than the second toe, which is higher than the third toe, and so on.

One of the primary reasons the foot is a mobile adaptor is to allow the body to get the first and fifth metatarsal heads and the calcaneus stable on the ground.

Often a person will have difficulty getting the first metatarsophalangeal joint on the ground. The body compensates by causing the calcaneus to excessively evert, thereby "pulling" the first metatarsal and metatarsal head to the ground. This results in a compensated abductovarus forefoot. In essence, the body artificially causes a reaction by driving the first ray—the first metatarsal bone, metatarsal head, and phalange—to the ground.

Keeping the principles of foot mechanics in mind, you will see that when the calcaneus everts, the talus will move medially, and the tibia will rotate medially as well. However, due to the body's compensation of everting the calcaneus, the timing of this reaction is often later than in a normal gait reaction.

You may also see an additional compensation where the heel whips medially, the lower extremity rotates outward, and the hip falsely appears to extend. The hip is actually circumducting, which can lead to numerous dysfunctions and discomfort, such as sacroiliac joint pain, anterior hip pain, and adductor strain. In these cases, orthotics that have a deep heel cup to control rearfoot motion may be helpful. Additionally, a slight arch is beneficial to help stabilize the midfoot, and a skive or cutout for the first ray will assist in first metatarsal head stability.

» **INSIGHT: People who are tight in the hips through the transverse plane are also tight in the frontal plane. You must improve the frontal range of motion before addressing the transverse plane. This approach will enhance the client's ability to move more easily in the transverse plane.**

Referring again to Figure 9.1, the hip loads when it flexes in the sagittal plane, adducts in the frontal plane, and internally rotates in the transverse plane. If any of these actions are limited, all are compromised.

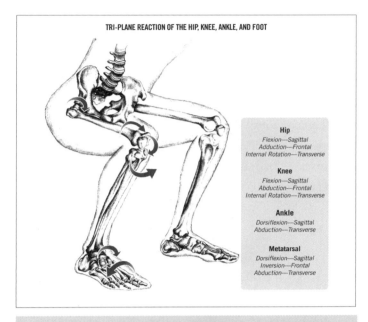

TRI-PLANE REACTION OF THE HIP, KNEE, ANKLE, AND FOOT

**Hip**
Flexion—Sagittal
Adduction—Frontal
Internal Rotation—Transverse

**Knee**
Flexion—Sagittal
Abduction—Frontal
Internal Rotation—Transverse

**Ankle**
Dorsiflexion—Sagittal
Abduction—Transverse

**Metatarsal**
Dorsiflexion—Sagittal
Inversion—Frontal
Abduction—Transverse

**FIGURE 9.1 TRI-PLANE LOADING CHAIN REACTIONS**

Hip transverse-plane motion is highly dependent upon motion in the frontal plane. If the hip is tight and cannot adduct, the head of the femur lacks the ability to translate and depress into the acetabulum, resulting in limited motion. The reason for this lack of action varies from soft-tissue tightness of the external rotators in the gluteal complex to hip-capsule tightness, or perhaps degeneration.

Plan to gain frontal-plane motion first, and then start working to improve rotational movements in the transverse plane.

» **INSIGHT: Through upright positions and the gait cycle, the great toe, calf, hips, and shoulder girdle are friends of the abdominals. Reduced dorsiflexion of the great toe, a tight calf, or a tight hip flexor will reduce sagittal-plane extension and will not fully eccentrically load the abdominals in the sagittal plane.**

If the hip cannot extend, the torso will not be in a relative extended position in relation to the hip. This will reduce the eccentric loading of the abdominals in the

sagittal plane. Additionally, the weight shift to the opposite side will be lessened and the frontal plane load upon the abdominals is reduced as well.

When the shoulder girdle is tight, that shoulder will not adequately extend, thereby reducing thoracic rotation on the same side. This reduces the powerful transverse plane eccentric loading of the abdominal complex. Additionally, the musculature of the back and spine does not load efficiently in the transverse plane.

» **INSIGHT: If the lateral hip is tight, causing reduced hip adduction, the abdominals are not optimally loaded in the frontal plane. If the shoulder cannot extend—thereby limiting thoracic rotation—the abdominals do not effectively load in the transverse plane. Any one of these can cause a chain reaction effect upon the others, and can reduce the power and range of motion of the abdominals.**

Optimal function of the abdominal complex is greatly dependent upon the extremities to load efficiently. It is common for people to have limitations of movement along with abdominal weakness in various planes of motion.

The question to ask is, why are they weak doing this action, and what are the goals of the activity? Many cases will reveal a limitation in the foot and ankle complex, which limits ankle dorsiflexion, hip extension, and sagittal plane loading. As you know from earlier discussions, this will also impact the other two cardinal planes.

In other cases, the hip will be the culprit, inhibiting adequate hip adduction and affecting the frontal-plane loading of the abdominal complex, ultimately impacting all three planes of motion. Even shoulder issues or mid-thoracic tightness will affect abdominal function and can create compensations.

Based on the global reactions of regions distant from the abdominals, the "core" starts from the floor and begins with the action of the great toe in upright movement.

you decide to use concentric adductor movement patterns, do them first in the workout, followed by eccentric integrated movement patterns, such as a lateral lunge. This will strengthen as well as lengthen the tissue, and will cover both ends of the movement spectrum.

When moving in the frontal plane—say, using the example of a side lunge to the right—the left adductor eccentrically loads as the left hip abducts and the right hip adducts, as seen in Photo 9.6.

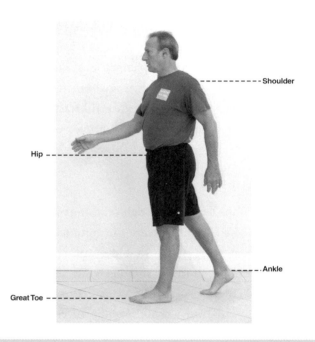

**PHOTO 9.5 ABSOLUTELY FRIENDS**

» **INSIGHT:** In gait, the adductors do not adduct the hip—they assist in decelerating hip flexion and internal rotation of the lead leg, and hip extension and external rotation of the trailing leg. The adductor of the trailing or extended leg assists in decelerating hip extension and external rotation. When doing a side lunge in the frontal plane, the adductor of the opposite side of the loaded hip decelerates hip abduction on the same side.

If this is the case, why are hip adduction machines or concentric adductor exercises so popular? These are used to strengthen the adductor complex, and also as a remedial movement pattern.

However, the adductor machine or concentric adductor movement patterns will shorten and tighten tissue that can often lead to pelvic immobility and gait problems. If

**PHOTO 9.6 FRONTAL-PLANE LUNGE WITH OPPOSITE ARM TO OPPOSITE LATERAL REACH WITH A VIPR™**

Considering the alignment of the fibers of the adductor complex shows us they are conducive for rotational movements. They connect from the pubic ramus and obliquely trace to the linea aspera of the femur. The adductors assist in the transverse and sagittal plane movements.

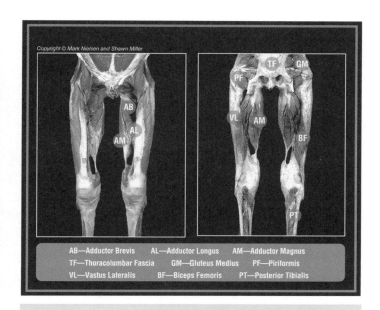

Copyright © Mark Nielsen and Shawn Miller

| AB—Adductor Brevis | AL—Adductor Longus | AM—Adductor Magnus |
| TF—Thoracolumbar Fascia | GM—Gluteus Medius | PF—Piriformis |
| VL—Vastus Lateralis | BF—Biceps Femoris | PT—Posterior Tibialis |

**PHOTO 9.7 ALIGNMENT OF THE ADDUCTOR FIBERS**

» **INSIGHT:** People often have either hip or iliotibial band tightness (ITB), or pain in that area. Ask these clients if their training includes some form of concentric hip abduction movement pattern, such as a hip abduction machine that might shorten the lateral gluteal complex. This leads to a myriad of maladies, such as hip or ITB pain or tightness, and might be the source of the problem.

For example, ITB "tightness" might be a sensation resulting from tautness—long and taut, rather than short and tight. The ITB attaches to the tensor fascia lata and part of the gluteus maximus. If these structures, along with the abductor complex, become short and tight, it lengthens the ITB.

Make sure the client works from both ends of the movement spectrum and performs an exercise that will eccentrically load the abductors in three planes of motion. When these become lengthened, the abductors will have greater range of motion and the strength to control hip adduction. Additionally, the lateral gluteal complex will become lengthened and reduce the tautness of the iliotibial band.

*In gait, the abductors act like a sling to decelerate hip adduction and internal rotation during the mid-stance of the gait cycle. During mid-stance,* the abductor complex is eccentrically loaded. Just prior to the heel-off phase, the abductor complex assists in accelerating hip extension and external rotation through a concentric action.

*From a functional perspective, we might consider the abductors to be part of the gluteal complex.*

### THE SHOULDER

» **INSIGHT:** When a client presents with shoulder-joint pain, first look at scapular motion of the same shoulder. In many instances the scapula is tight and may not be gliding smoothly over the thoracic spine. If there is limited motion, take a step back and ask why. Hint: Look at the hips and foot function as part of the evaluation.

Think of the shoulder girdle like a crane. The backside of this heavy machinery has a counterweight to offset the heft of the crane's arm. Think of the scapula in the same light, as a counterweight to the humerus.

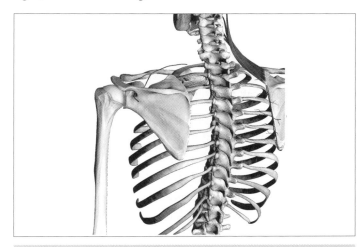

**FIGURE 9.2 THE SHOULDER GIRDLE, PHOTO COPYRIGHT © 3D4MEDICAL**

Additionally, the scapula has 19 muscles attached to it, and serves as an anchor to these major primary movers and smaller stabilizing muscles.

When the humerus moves in all three planes of motion, it must articulate with the glenoid—the shallow socket on the lateral side of the scapula—forming the glenohumeral joint. As the arm moves, the scapula must glide over the ribs to allow efficiency of the humeral head, as well as to counterbalance the weight of the humerus. This creates a mechanical advantage for the lever system inherent in the body.

Additionally, the acromion process, which is the flattened portion on the lateral end of the clavicle to protect the shoulder joint, is similar to a low ceiling, where the humeral head must have enough room to move under the ceiling. The low ceiling in this analogy is the acromion process. In order for this to be successful, the acromion and scapula must clear out of the way so the humeral head does not "bump" into it, causing injury, particularly to the supraspinatus tendon.

For example, when abducting the arm, the scapula must also abduct by gliding along the ribs while it elevates. This allows the glenoid to move upward on an oblique angle as the humeral head abducts and depresses slightly, which accounts for the clearance of the head.

During this action the humeral head must "sink" into the glenoid to avoid the greater trochanter of the shoulder "bumping" into the acromion process, which can often lead to impingement issues. If the scapula has limited motion due to soft tissue "stickiness," adhesions from injury, or postural problems, the risk of shoulder-joint injury increases.

If the scapula is not moving well, we must not stop there. This is a *what,* not a *why.* This situation is a local problem. Here we step back and look at the reactions of movement from a global perspective.

In many cases, when the scapula has limited mobility, the thoracic spine is also lacking adequate motion. But we still cannot stop there; we must also investigate how the hips and feet are functioning. In the great majority of cases, you may find a foot or hip limitation, or both. When we find these limitations, this is a *why,* and then we can address the *what.*

Remember the concepts of the hip and shoulder relationships we discussed earlier? In the sagittal plane, extension of the same-side hip enhances flexion of the same-side shoulder. In addition, the same-side hip that flexes enhances same-side shoulder extension.

In the frontal plane, the same-side hip that adducts enhances same-side shoulder abduction, and vice versa. In the transverse plane, the opposite hip that internally rotates enhances the opposite shoulder into internal rotation. Consider this scenario another way—the same-side hip that internally rotates enhances the same-side shoulder into external rotation.

The takeaway from this is that in most nontraumatic overuse injuries of the shoulder, we must look globally to determine the precise problem affecting the symptomatic shoulder.

### THE KNEE

» **INSIGHT:** In approximately 75% of anterior cruciate ligament (ACL) injuries that did not occur due to acute blunt trauma, there is a rearfoot control problem involved. Calcaneal eversion will increase ankle dorsiflexion and tibial internal rotation, putting the ACL under tension. This is a connection you must investigate.

This is often a mechanical and perhaps an extreme issue with those who have rearfoot control issues. Consider the angulation of the ACL as it attaches at the posterior lateral femoral condyle in the femoral groove and the medial tibial inter-tubercular groove. With a planus or flat foot, the calcaneus is everted, the talus is adducted, and the tibia is in a medially rotated position. This places tension on the ACL.

This is not exclusive to the planus foot, however. You might also see this when a person has a compensated forefoot abductovarus. An abducted forefoot in relation to the rearfoot characterizes this foot type.

Remember our foot mechanics principles: The body seeks to get the first and fifth metatarsal joints and calcaneus firmly on the ground. With a compensated forefoot abductovarus, the rearfoot will compensate and evert more to get the first metatarsal head stable to the ground. This will place the ACL under considerable tension due to tibia internal rotation.

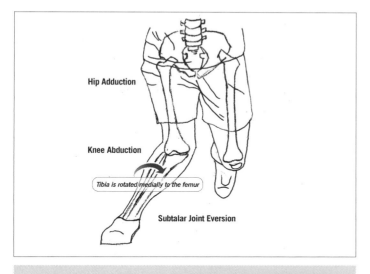

**FIGURE 9.3 DYNAMIC KNEE VALGUS**

In many cases, the person might move into a quick external rotation that exceeds the body's threshold, resulting in an ACL injury. In these situations, the knee is the victim, not the culprit. Place the foot in a neutral environment, strengthen the gluteal complex and abdominals, and you can potentially reduce the risk of this devastating injury. This is vividly shown in Figure 9.3.

» **INSIGHT: A golfer who presented with left hip and low-back pain kept complaining she could not open up during follow-through and felt short and tight at address. During the backswing, her left midfoot was locked and did not pronate, and the quadratus lumborum (QL) was tight through impact and follow-through. She stretched her hip flexor, but did not get relief. We stretched the QL through the frontal and transverse planes, applied a muscle energy technique, and added an anterior lunge with rotational reach. She also did a pivotal toe-touch pattern to mobilize her foot, and later reported no hip or back pain and is back to normal distances with all shots. The QL has a strong**

**transverse-plane action, in addition to the frontal plane that has been advocated for decades.**

The key issues here are the locked left forefoot and the QL working in the transverse plane. If the foot remains locked, it will not pronate through the gait cycle or during the backswing.

The forefoot must go through forefoot abduction when the rearfoot everts. This allows ankle dorsiflexion, tibial internal rotation, knee flexion, abduction, and internal rotation. Following the reactions, the hip will flex, adduct, and internally rotate.

Since the QL is attached to the hip and has an obliquity of its fibrous alignment into the lumbar spine, hip action will eccentrically load the QL during both the golf swing and gait.

The pivotal toe touch will mobilize the foot in both pronation and supination. This will help the entire system be successful throughout the chain.

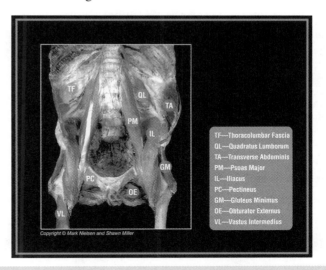

**PHOTO 9.8 OBSERVE THE ANGULATION OF THE QL**

» **INSIGHT: The knee is the "dumbest" joint in the body; it will follow what the foot and hip tell it to do. However, we should not be concerned with where the knee goes. Instead, be concerned with why it goes that way. In normal, healthy conditions, the foot and ankle complex go through calcaneal eversion, ankle**

**dorsiflexion, tibial internal rotation, and forefoot abduction. These actions allow the knee to flex, internally rotate, and abduct, then the hip flexes, internally rotates, and adducts. These reactions enhance force absorption and deceleration.**

If the foot is flat, the tibia will have more internal rotation and the knee will be in a relative valgus position compared with a neutral foot. If the foot has a high arch, the tibia will be externally rotated in a more relative varus position compared with a neutral foot.

If the hip and gluteal complex are tight, often the femur is in an externally rotated position. This could put the knee in a varus alignment. If the adductors are tight, the femur is often internally rotated, which can cause the knee to appear to be in a valgus alignment.

As you can see in Photos 9.9 and 9.10, the joints above and below affect the knee. It will react to the forces applied through the movement. We need to address the problems, not the symptom of the knee reactions.

**PHOTO 9.10 KNEE IN VARUS POSITION**

*Notice the foot structure and see how it impacts tibial rotation and the respective positions of the knee in valgus in Photo 9.9 and varus in Photo 9.10.*

A corrective strategy to help align the knee while lunging can be done with arm reaches to one side or the other. If the client has a valgus knee alignment, perform an anterior lunge with a bilateral arm reach to the same side as the lunging leg.

As you can see in Photo 9.11, the left leg lunges forward. Both arms reach to left lateral, causing the torso to rotate to the left; the pelvis rotates to the left, and the femur and tibia move into external rotation. The knee being stuck between both bone segments moves into a relative varus position and aligns over the foot.

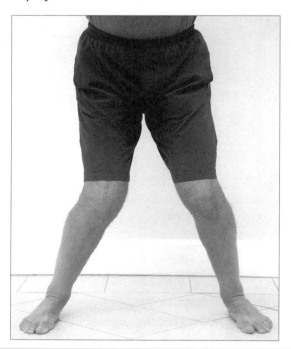

**PHOTO 9.9 KNEE IN VALGUS POSITION**

**PHOTO 9.11 LEFT LEG ANTERIOR LUNGE WITH A BILATERAL ARM REACH TO THE LEFT**

**PHOTO 9.12 LEFT LEG ANTERIOR LUNGE WITH OPPOSITE ARM REACH TO THE RIGHT**

If a client has a varus knee alignment, use an anterior lunge with a bilateral arm reach to the opposite side as shown in Photo 9.12.

Stand up and try these drills to feel this for yourself. You can use strategies like these to train the knee into safer quality movements for your clients who have valgus or varus knee alignment problems.

» **INSIGHT: When clients complain of hamstring tightness, do not assume the hamstrings are short and tight. They could be long and taut, giving the sensation of tightness. Check pelvic alignment to determine if there is a significant anterior pelvic tilt. If there is, the ischial tuberosity is farther from the tibial condylar insertion, thereby lengthening the hamstrings. Often accompanying the anterior pelvic tilt, the tibia is internally rotated, adding to the hamstrings tension in the transverse plane.**

After you consider pelvic alignment, look at the foot structure as well, as an everted rearfoot will place the tibia into a relative internally rotated position. This will lengthen the hamstrings in the transverse plane. When this is taken into account, along with the pelvic alignment issue, the hamstrings will be in a lengthened position and taut—*not* short and tight.

You should also assess gluteal strength, which will impact pelvic alignment.

» **INSIGHT:** Many multisport athletes have ITB, piriformis, and tight hamstrings issues. Often, they have a foot problem that does not allow the gluteal complex to effectively load. When the gluteals are weak, the hamstrings, the deep internal hip rotators, and the ITB can be overused. The foot is not the only cause, but definitely check foot function during your assessment.

Usually, the gluteals are weak in those afflicted with these symptoms. The problem then lies in foot function. The foot must move through the four components discussed earlier—calcaneal eversion, ankle dorsiflexion, tibia internal rotation, and forefoot abduction. These reactions allow the knee to flex in the sagittal plane, abduct in the frontal plane, and internally rotate in the transverse plane. This ultimately loads the gluteal complex in all three planes of motion.

Endurance athletes, especially multisport endurance athletes, often have a weak gluteal complex. The training for these athletes is too sagittal-plane dominant. When designing strength training programs for these clients, you may be more successful working in the frontal and transverse planes. Training with more emphasis on the frontal and transverse planes causes the foot and gluteal complex to be mobilized and strengthened in all three planes of motion.

If the gluteals are functioning at an optimal level, they will have the enhanced ability to decelerate hip flexion in the sagittal plane. This will then reduce the compensation of the hamstrings in decelerating hip flexion.

When the gluteals are strong in the frontal plane, they will decelerate hip adduction during the loading phase, and accelerate hip abduction through the propulsive phase.

If adequate motion is available through the gluteal complex in the frontal plane—especially in the eccentric phase of training—the fibers will lengthen and reduce the tension of the lateral gluteal complex, particularly of the gluteus medius and tensor fascia lata, thereby reducing the lengthening of the iliotibial band. If this occurs, the ITB will not have to compensate for the lack of function of the gluteals in the frontal plane.

Lastly, when the gluteal complex is strong—especially the gluteus maximus—the deep external hip rotators do not have to compensate for an underused maximus, resulting in less tension or overuse, particularly of the piriformis.

» **INSIGHT:** When clients present with patellar tendon pain, hip-flexor tightness, the loss of speed when running, or Achilles tendon issues, ask if their strength program includes weight-loaded toe raises. If so, this movement might cause significant tightness in the calf complex, inhibiting the ability to ankle dorsiflex during the gait cycle or other activities. If weighted toe raises are part of the strength training program, make sure these are integrated into the full spectrum of movement of the calf group.

When doing loaded toe raises, the ankle is moving through plantar flexion and concentric shortening of the muscle group. If the calf group is tight, ankle dorsiflexion is reduced and that can limit hip extension.

Additionally, spinal rotation to the opposite side might be reduced and this might create a multitude of problems. To work within the entire movement spectrum, include a loaded ankle dorsiflexion movement to eccentrically lengthen the muscle group.

When doing weighted toe raises, we need to load the foot, ankle, and calf group *first,* as this will decelerate ankle dorsiflexion, calcaneal eversion, tibial internal rotation, and forefoot abduction. This will allow the knee and hip to load in all three planes of motion and enhance the ability to perform explosive movements, along with other activities of daily living.

This is not to say we should never do plantar-flexion toe raises. But if we *only* do those, the risk of calf tightness increases and the ability to properly load the system in three planes of motion can be compromised.

If the need arises for resisted ankle plantar-flexion movements, or if the client absolutely wants to do calf raises, do these first. The tissue will gain strength; however, it will also shorten. After doing the designated sets of calf raises, you would then do an eccentrically loaded functional calf raise, as this will resist ankle dorsiflexion when the calf group lengthens and loads the foot and ankle system.

**PHOTO 9.13 SHOWS THE FUNCTIONAL CALF RAISE START POSITION AND PHOTO 9.14 SHOWS THE FINISH POSITION**

*Start your client in the "stand tall" position, then have the person lean forward from the ankles into ankle dorsiflexion and maintain the tall position. Do not allow a flex at the hip and make sure the heels stay on the ground. The person will feel the tension in the foot and calf, and then return to the start position. This eccentrically loads the calf group in a functional manner.*

## THE FOOT

» **INSIGHT:** Do you check the range of motion of the great toe and metatarsals of your clients? This is often overlooked and has great implications for biomechanical compensations. You will often see tight hip flexors, patellar tendon issues, or lack of transverse-plane motion when the great toe and metatarsal heads are tight or limited in motion.

Many trainers believe they do not need to know what the foot does, and most of the programming they do is from the calf up. However, as you study this material, you are gaining increased appreciation of human movement, and hopefully a greater interest in foot function.

There are 33 joints, 24 muscles, and 26 bones in the foot, which is the conduit that interfaces with the ground and sets the platform for the body to react.

There are considerable reactions that take place during normal foot reaction and through the gait cycle. The discussion in this section will assume "normal" foot function, with no pathology that may present in those afflicted with a foot disorder. With the numerous reactions that occur in the foot during the gait cycle, there are four essential actions we need to observe in foot action.

The foot is categorized into three regions, the forefoot, midfoot, and rearfoot.

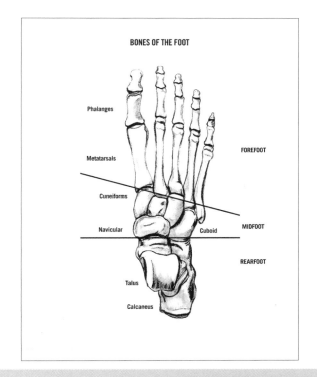

**FIGURE 9.4 BONES OF THE FOOT**

The forefoot consists of the toes—the phalanges. Phalanges two through five have three bones and two joints, while the great toe has two bones and one joint.

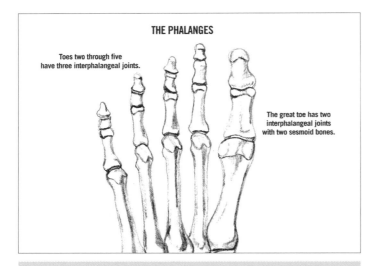

THE PHALANGES

Toes two through five have three interphalangeal joints.

The great toe has two interphalangeal joints with two sesmoid bones.

**FIGURE 9.5 THE PHALANGES**

The midfoot includes the three cuneiforms—medial, intermediate, and lateral—the navicular on the medial column, and the cuboid on the lateral column. These five bones form the midfoot arch and must be mobile to absorb forces during the "collapsing" of the arch in pronation.

Additionally, these structures must adapt and "lock up" as the foot moves through inversion or supination. This allows a rigid lever to propel the foot forward during the heel-off through toe-off phases of gait.

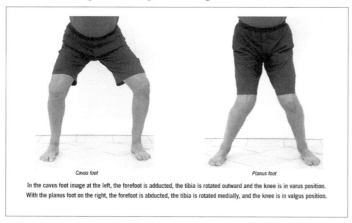

Cavus foot

Planus foot

In the cavus foot image at the left, the forefoot is adducted, the tibia is rotated outward and the knee is in varus position. With the planus foot on the right, the forefoot is abducted, the tibia is rotated medially, and the knee is in valgus position.

**PHOTO 9.15 COMPARING THE CAVUS AND PLANUS FOOT**

The calcaneus and talus make up the rearfoot. The calcaneus has a concave surface on the superior aspect, and the talus is convex at the inferior surface. The union of the calcaneus and talus form the subtalar joint, an extremely important joint that sets the environment for successful tri-plane motion.

When describing the action of the rearfoot, think of a motorcycle rider. Imagine the rider starting to lose balance; the bike falls to the right while the tires turn outward. In our analogy, the tires and bike are the calcaneus, while the rider is the talus. The rider—the talus—wears a long helmet called the tibia; the tibia sits atop the talus.

**PHOTO 9.16 RIDER "FALLING" TO THE RIGHT**

*The bottom of the tires turn left or outward, similar to the left calcaneus when everting.*

As the bike "falls" to the right, the tires turn outward, similar to the left foot hitting the ground and causing the calcaneus to evert—the heel "falls" right, while the bottom of the heel turns outward. With the foot on the ground during the landing phase of gait, the medial column of the foot, composed of the union of the talus and navicular forming the talo-navicular joint, fall medially toward the ground.

Based on the axis of motion, the primary motions of the talo-navicular and subtalar joints are eversion and inversion in the frontal plane. This motion allows the tibia to move farther forward in the sagittal plane and to dorsiflex at the ankle, while also internally rotating in the transverse plane.

Most texts discuss the sagittal plane of the ankle. In isolation, the talocrural joint—the ankle—is strictly a sagittal-plane mover. However, when the foot loads as it hits the ground, the ankle dorsiflexes in the sagittal plane; the calcaneus everts, causing the subtalar joint to evert in the frontal plane, and the tibia internally rotates in the transverse plane.

This reaction, in turn, causes the midfoot to evert in the frontal plane. The forefoot abducts in relation to the mid- and rearfoot due to the motion of the distal bone in relation to the proximal bone segments. Because the rearfoot and midfoot move farther and faster than the forefoot in the frontal plane, the metatarsals and phalanges are lateral to the proximal segments. Therefore, they are abducted to the rearfoot.

In cases where the mid-tarsal joints are limited in motion, the ability to pronate—or unlock and unload—is compromised. This does not allow the rearfoot to pronate or the tibia to internally rotate. If this occurs, the knee will not efficiently flex, abduct, or medially rotate. Here the lower extremity is in a relatively extended position that is not optimal to load and propel.

This often results in patellar tendonitis, hip pain, and low-back problems. The tissues remain in a shortened, propelled state, not allowing the lengthening of tissue associated with the pronation phase. This lack of preloading results in overuse of tissue during the propulsion phase of gait.

Additionally, these same maladies are common when the great toe is limited in its ability to dorsiflex. This benign yet important action allows the knee and hip to extend to an optimal length, causing adequate preload of those tissues. Equally important, this action serves as the last required impetus to shift weight to the opposite leg and hip, leading to optimal hip adduction on the opposite side.

When transforming into the weight shift to the other side, the hip adducts and internally rotates, raising the hip and allowing the swing leg clearance above the ground. Without this, the knee of the swing leg must compensate with prolonged knee and hip flexion to clear the foot prior to heel strike. Over time, this can lead to an overuse injury, often at the patellar tendon or hip flexors.

As a review, when the foot hits the ground in the pronation phase, the lower extremity is eccentrically loaded by virtue of:

- *Calcaneal eversion*
- *Ankle dorsiflexion*
- *Tibial internal rotation*
- *Forefoot abduction*

These motions clearly show the foot and ankle complex moving in three planes of motion. We want mobility in the foot during the pronation phase, yet as ambulation takes place and the hip moves over the foot, the swing leg drives the opposing hip forward, which will invert the calcaneus, plantar flex the ankle, externally rotate the tibia, and adduct the forefoot.

» **INSIGHT:** As a cuing tip, when your client is performing a squat or a lunge, use the cue, "Squish the bug under the big toe joint." This causes a lower-extremity reaction to load the gluteal complex more effectively in all three planes of motion.

"Squishing the bug" causes the first metatarsal head to be relatively plantar-flexed to the lesser toes. This also causes the forefoot to be abducted in relation to the rearfoot. As this occurs, the rearfoot everts, enhancing ankle dorsiflexion, and the tibia and femur internally rotate.

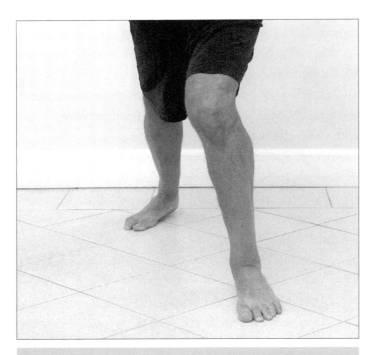

**PHOTO 9.17 SQUISHING THE BUG**

*The first metatarsophalangeal joint is stable on the ground; the tibia internally rotates, and the knee flexes, abducts, and internally rotates. Notice also how this impacts the lower leg and knee.*

This reaction would not be fully loaded if the foot was not able to achieve the "squishing of the bug" position. This "pulls" the gluteal fibers into a lengthened, eccentrically loaded position in the transverse plane. Additionally, these reactions create an environment for successful hip flexion and adduction.

» **INSIGHTS: Clients who have had sports hernia injuries will often have had a foot or ankle injury within the previous two to five years. After assessing these clients, you will find limitations in movements of the previously injured foot or ankle. This is not a coincidence. Make sure these clients recapture proper motion in the affected areas.**

During the gait cycle, as the hip passes over the foot, the hip extends, moving the femur into a position behind the hip and resulting in hip extension. As the hip continues to pass forward, the tibia tilts forward, causing ankle dorsiflexion. At heel-off, the forefoot dorsiflexes, adding to further hip and knee extension and resulting in propulsion prior to toe-off.

In explosive actions such as sprinting or jumping, it is necessary for these reactions to transpire to allow the smooth, natural reaction throughout the body for a successful transition to the opposite side. If there are limitations in foot reactions, such as inadequate ankle dorsiflexion, limited forefoot dorsiflexion, or hip-flexor tightness, hip extension is suboptimal.

During jumping, sprinting, skating, or other explosive tri-plane motions, the action starts to become a top-down rather than bottom-up reaction. This can cause a breakdown of the tissue in the lower abdominal region, and over time can lead to strain or a more severe tear.

## CUEING

As trainers, we must remember we are very familiar with training facilities, modalities, and movement patterns. We must not take for granted that the clients who visit us are not as acquainted, and instead realize they need quality cueing, whether it be verbal, tactile, or visual.

The majority of your clients are not focused on body awareness or movements. Many have no idea what positions they move into, and therefore need to be taught that sense of awareness. This is where effective and clear cueing instruction is key to each client's success. Make cueing clear, concise, and use as few cues as possible to achieve the task at hand.

» **INSIGHT: We often give too many cues to clients when they squat or lunge. Keep it simple: Tell them to "Stand tall." Specifically, have them reach from the greater trochanter of the hip through the head and toward the sky. This aligns the spine into a gentle lordosis, retracts the shoulder girdle, and causes a bit of lordosis in the** cervical spine. Then cue to "Squat from the hips" after making sure there is adequate ankle dorsiflexion to make the squat successful.

If this "stand tall" posture is retained during the squat, the spine will have greater stability throughout the activity.

From the "stand tall" position, the pelvis will attain a slight anterior tilt to the spine. This will allow the lumbar spine to extend and maintain its lordosis. The reaction further up into the thoracic spine will cause the scapulae to retract and the cervical spine to regain its lordosis.

This is an easy approach to aligning the spine, and your clients will not have to try to remember the numerous cues trainers have given them in the past, such as "push the chest forward and the gluteals back," "look up," and "make sure the knees are over the toes."

**PHOTO 9.18 WHERE THE PELVIS GOES, THE LOW BACK WILL FOLLOW**

This idea follows the critical concepts of the Big Movement Rocks of the foot and ankle complex, hips, and thoracic spine. For example, those afflicted with low-back pain have similar movement tendencies of tightness in the hips and thoracic spine. Many of these people also have a

foot dysfunction, such as tight subtalar joints, tightness in the midfoot, or lack of dorsiflexion in the metatarsal joints. As you know, if any of these areas become limited, compensations commonly ensue.

Consider this advice that has been circulating in fitness and physical therapy for many years: When people have low-back pain, injury, or surgery, they should not rotate. This information is correct, yet misinterpreted. There should be limited rotation through the lumbar spine, yet we should not disallow *all* rotation.

If no rotation is allowed, the musculature of the back will become further tightened and will create other problems, such as compression at the facet joints or among the transverse processes.

There are approximately 144 muscles in the spine, and about 120 have an angulation to them. Fibers running on an angle are conducive to rotation. If no rotation is allowed, a person becomes too sagittal-plane dominant, and other discomforts often follow.

When rotation is limited in the lumbar spine, the transverse-plane movements must come from the hips and thoracic spine. If there is ample motion in these regions, the compensatory patterns through the lumbar spine are reduced.

Likewise, there must be proper function in the foot and ankle complex to allow the hips and thoracic spine to be successful.

» **INSIGHT: When performing shoulder work through the transverse plane, we should not "reach with the arm," a common training cue. Instead, tell your clients to "Move the scapula." Where the scapula goes, the humerus will follow. Likewise, where the humerus goes, the scapula will follow. This will not only train the shoulder girdle, but will also allow motion through the thoracic spine.**

There are 19 muscles attached to the shoulder girdle, and all of them want to play by eccentrically loading, stabilizing, and then concentrically unloading. The body needs scapular motion to allow proper functioning, to reduce impingement issues, and to keep all tissue of the shoulder girdle mobile *and* stable.

Additionally, allowing the shoulder girdle—the scapula in particular—to glide over the rib cage will help the thoracic spine move freely in all three planes of motion.

Why do so many trainers tell their clients to retract the scapula when performing a shoulder or chest press? The goal may be to develop a stable shoulder girdle, but this cue creates more dysfunction than it helps with stability.

Use the cue to "Move the scapula. Where the scapula goes, the humerus will follow."

Likewise, where the humerus goes, the scapula should follow. Having an immobile scapula can create shoulder impingement symptoms and dysfunction.

## OBSERVATIONS OF THE PROFESSION

Our field does a great job knowing what, when, and how, but it needs to better understand and appreciate the why. If someone presents with a problem or an injury, that is a what, not a why.

You will want to step back and look at how each client moves and then apply that information into a chain-reaction biomechanical assessment. This means looking at movement of the joints above, below, and on the opposite side to get an understanding of the global system, not just the local system.

Often when trainers attend a conference, they learn a new movement pattern over a weekend, and then use it with their clients on Monday. They have no rationale of why to use it, other than the fact it looked cool and kicked their butts on Saturday. This practice does not take into account the limitations, compensations, and idiosyncrasies of each client.

Most trainers do a great job of the *whats*—what will take place in the program that day, or what the problem is, such as back pain. They do a great job of *when* a client will do a certain movement pattern or a periodized program.

And many do a great job of *how* to do a certain movement or program.

But often they do not do a good job of the *why*.

According to the *2013 IDEA Trends of Personal Training and Equipment* study, 84% of training clients use a personal trainer because of a chronic injury. Yet far too often when a client presents for personal training, the trainer does not do a movement assessment to determine the *whys—why* does the client have back pain, or *why* is there knee pain, shoulder pain, or hip tightness?

To repeat: When a person presents with a symptom, that is a *what,* not a *why.* We need to take a step back and do a global movement assessment to investigate why the client has certain symptoms, and then create a strategy that addresses the limitations and compensations that follow.

When this is accomplished, we address the *whys* and become proactive to correcting problems. By addressing the global movement first, we can get a sense of not only of how people are moving, but why they are moving that way.

Once this is gleaned from a gait-and-motion analysis as described in Chapter Eight, beginning on page 123, we can then unravel the local issues of movement.

» **INSIGHT:** Why do the majority of fitness professionals or clinicians only do isolated, single-joint stretching with their clients? This sometimes works, but is only attacking a link in a chain, when at some point we must address the entire chain.

For example, a tight hip flexor will reduce the range of motion when dorsiflexing the same-side ankle during the gait cycle. In addition to stretching the tight hip, we need to stretch the same-side calf with the ankle and calf in an integrated flexibility chain.

Remember, with overuse issues, the site of the injury is not the problem. The problem is a joint level or two above or below that is limited in motion, and compensation often ensues elsewhere.

That is the crux of the matter. The body moves through a series of reactions that are greatly dependent upon joints above and below.

If a calf has limited mobility and cannot move through full ankle dorsiflexion, the tibia and femur will not move as far past the foot as is optimal. This will inhibit the hip from moving into a favorable anterior pelvic tilt and will reduce hip extension.

Likewise, if a hip flexor is tight and the hip cannot fully load into extension, it will reduce the ability to dorsiflex the ankle. Not only will the hip flexors and calf become tight over time, but both results often lead to reduced rotation to the opposite side. This can lead to limitation of loading the body in the frontal plane as well.

The body is an integrated webbing that affects motions globally within the system, not just locally.

If an exercise isolates a particular muscle tissue, do that exercise first. This will strengthen the local region, yet it will also shorten that tissue structure, and it typically trains the muscle in only one plane of motion. After completion of the exercise, perform a complementary movement pattern that will eccentrically load the tissue in all three planes of motion. In this sense, the myofascial tissue will have worked through the full movement spectrum and will gain both strength and length in three planes of motion.

For example, after a client does a knee extension to strengthen the quadriceps, plan to do a tri-plane lunge. This will eccentrically load the quadriceps in three planes of motion.

Remember, isolation works an isolated region of the body, is concentric first, predominantly in one plane of motion. Integrated movements are typically body-wide reactions, eccentric first, and in three planes of motion.

This chapter describes the principles and concepts and suggests ideas of how to put them into application. If you apply the principles of movement into the complexities your clients present, many of their maladies will improve.

We have only covered a microcosm of the many scenarios we address on a daily basis. The insights above are some of the many common issues presented to fitness professionals, as well as in the physical therapy world.

No matter what the scenario, the principles of movement are applicable to every population. It is up to us as trainers and movement professionals to develop the concept and have a rationale for its application.

# THE VARIABILITY OF PROGRAM DESIGN

*"There is nothing so terrible as activity without insight."*

~ J O H A N N   W O L F G A N G   V O N   G O E T H E

---

Contemporary models of program design include considerations other than earlier models such as aerobic, long, slow duration, high-intensity short duration, or circuit training, for example. These concepts are still foundational platforms for overall program design, with the emergence of recent theories based on research of high-intensity interval training (HIIT), movement variability, and the 4-Quadrant system by Michol Dalcourt to name a few. As more research evolves, the blending of these can create a useful hybrid of program design.

In Chapter Seven, *Blending Tradition with Integrated Training* beginning on page 117, we looked at the Action Pyramid process we use at Human Motion Associates to develop strategies in rehabilitation and exercise programming. For example, in the foundation layer, we know we want to mobilize the Big Movement Rocks of the foot and ankle complex, hips, and thoracic spine, and strengthen the regions requiring more stability, such as the ankle in the frontal plane, the lumbar spine, and the parascapular shoulder girdle.

The condition of each client will dictate your strategies as you commence program planning. Before designing a program, you must consider if a client has been sedentary, or when a patient needs to gain strength to an injured joint or soft tissue, or when lacking range of motion in a particular plane of motion through a single joint or series of joints.

In the early stages of a program, a blended process of Muscle Energy Techniques (MET), a traditional exercise pattern, and an integrated movement pattern program is beneficial. We will flesh out these concepts next.

## MUSCLE ENERGY TECHNIQUES (MET)

Leon Chaitow, founding editor-in-chief of the *Journal of Bodywork and Movement Therapies*, states in his book *Muscle Energy Techniques:*

*"Muscle Energy Techniques are a class of soft tissue osteopathic (originally) manipulated methods that incorporate precisely directed and controlled, patient initiated, isometric and/or isotonic contractions, designed to improve musculoskeletal function and reduce pain."*

When people present with an injury or a dysfunction, tissue is often shortened, inhibited, and weak. In the majority of cases, a joint is limited in motion, often caused by the body's protective mechanism to guard and stiffen the weakened segment. In this instance, there is *too much* stability in the region, and to build more strength and stability is pointless for an effective, functional outcome. Do not build stability on top of stability.

After considering the health and activity history and lifestyle of a client, MET is often helpful to gain not only stimulation of the tissue, but also increased range of motion.

As Chaitow goes on to say:

*"Structure and function are so intertwined that one cannot be considered without the other. The structure of a unit, or area, determines what function it is capable of. Seen in reverse, it is function that imposes demands on the very structures that allow them to operate, and which over time can modify the structure…"*

He further says:

*"The number of sarcomeres in theory determines the distance through which a muscle can shorten and the length at which it produces maximum force… the stimulus for sarcomere length changes may be the amount of tension along the myofibril or the myotendon junction with high tension leading to an addition of sarcomeres and low tension causing a decrease."*

In a dysfunctional state resulting from injury or inactivity, limitations and compensations are rampant in our clients' movement patterns. In open-chain reactions, restrictions cause a tight, shortened muscle, often accompanied by a degree of lengthening and weakening of the antagonists.

For instance, if a person is supine on a table and knee flexion is limited, in most cases the quadriceps will be shortened and the hamstrings will be lengthened and weak. This will not only limit knee flexion, but will also inhibit the femoral translation as the femur glides forward on the tibia. The result is difficult and often painful knee flexion. If you use a closed-chain assessment such as an abbreviated single-leg squat, not only will the knee be limited in motion, but the ankle and hip will also be adversely affected with limited reactions.

If we look at the tissue through the lens of reciprocal inhibition, the agonist and antagonist relationship changes, as both quadriceps and hamstrings are firing to some degree to maintain the stability of the knee, ankle, and hip.

There is a place for techniques such as MET in a corrective strategy paradigm. There is a need to combine the isolated link action to strengthen and mobilize tissue with the integrated patterns to gain both mobility and stability.

Muscle Energy Techniques (MET) is a term derived from the osteopathic, orthopedic, and physiotherapy professions. Fred Mitchell, an osteopathic clinician, is known as the major contributor of this practice, with refinements from Vladimir Janda and Karel Lewit. Craig Liebenson referred to MET as "an active muscular relaxation technique" used to lengthen short, tight tissue and strengthen physiologically weakened muscles or groups of muscles.

The implementation of MET uses a relative isometric contraction against manual resistance that matches the energy the client is able to produce. As Liebenson states,

*"When a muscle is isometrically contracted, its antagonist will be inhibited and will relax immediately following this. Thus, the anatagonist of a shortened muscle or group of muscles may be isometrically contracted in order to achieve a degree of ease and additional movement in the shortened tissues."*

To delve deeper into MET, seek out books by Leon Chaitow on Muscle Energy Techniques.

The use of MET is highly effective in early stages of a sport rehabilitation or a corrective exercise program. When a client produces a progressive force output against your resistance, not only will the tissue gain strength, but it will also lengthen. By resisting the distal bone segment of the joint, the tissue length will increase.

However, only doing this in one plane of motion does not offer full function of the tissue and joint mobilization. This relates to the muscle tissue, yet knowing the recent research on fascia, we must consider the principles for maintaining fascial strength, resiliency, and fitness.

As discussed in Chapter Five, the *Flexibility Highways* section beginning on page 93, fascia is constantly adapting to the environment of forces and stresses within and applied to the tissues. Fascia has a high tolerance to resist forces and slowly adjusts or creeps as it changes its length. As the tissues adjust to forces and demands on them, the fascia will slowly lengthen to control and decelerate motion. By doing so, the fascia will become stronger, particularly when it is eccentrically loaded in three planes of motion.

Any postural position requires the fascial system to maintain the postural structure. Movement constantly remodels the extracellular matrix that comprises fascial tissue.

If collagen assists in maintaining the structure yet movement modifies the fascial consistency, collagen favors mobility, which will enhance the eccentric loading of tissue, resulting in stability of the tissue and joints. To attain the optimal loading, this must load in tri-plane positions for adaptation.

To apply this approach in the function layer of the Action Pyramid, we apply MET to resist the tissue in at least two planes of motion.

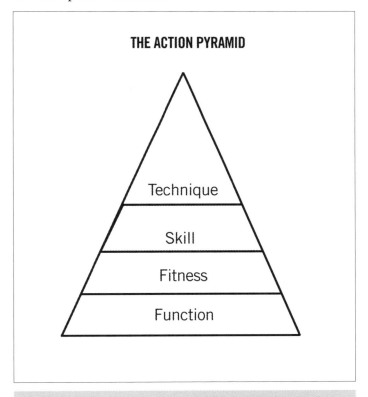

**FIGURE 10.1 THE ACTION PYRAMID**

When you see improvements of greater range of motion and force production through lower discomfort, it is time to move to a traditional exercise.

## TRADITIONAL EXERCISES IN THE ACTION PYRAMID

This phase of the continuum is not revolutionary, but it plays an important role in the overall plan. Strength and hypertrophy of the myofascial tissue is needed before working in a functional, integrated movement pattern. We do not do these phases independently of each other—they are complementary.

Continuing with the example of knee strength and range of motion, after motion is gained through MET, you might have the person use a leg press to gain both mobility and strength. When implementing this strategy, keep in mind this is generally an isolated, concentric first, and predominantly single-plane movement.

If the person can tolerate the exercise and sustains strength gains, move to a regressive, functional, integrated movement such as an ankle mobility pattern. The ankle must be mobile in the sagittal plane, but also needs motion from the tibia in the transverse plane. Additionally, the forefoot must abduct in the frontal plane to make the knee successful. After the ankle mobility pattern is sound, progress to a shifting motion to allow the foot, ankle, hip, and knee to be loaded in all three planes of motion.

As the range of motion improves—along with the ability to decelerate and cleanly return the action to the starting position—you can progress to a wall pattern such as those in Photos 10.1A-E or a wall banger shown in Photo 10.2.

**PHOTOS 10.1A-E WALL PATTERNS TO DIFFERENT VECTORS**

In Photo 10.1A you see the wall pattern starting position with the hands on the wall at shoulder height and feet about hip-width apart. Photo B shows reaches to the

12:00 o'clock position to eccentrically load the Anterior Flexibility Highway through extension movements—make sure the client keeps the heels on the floor.

Photo C moves through the Posterior Flexibility Highway into flexion. Remind the client to stand tall. Look for adequate ankle dorsiflexion, and make sure the hip moves into anterior pelvic tilt. This is a squatting action and should not be done by flexing at the hip to bend over.

Photo D moves through the Lateral Flexibility Highway to eccentrically load the lateral sling of the body and into hip adduction. Make sure the hip is over the foot and the opposite adductor is lengthened with the knee extended. This pattern mobilizes both the right hip into adduction and left hip into abduction.

Photo E is an opposite lateral reach and will mobilize and strengthen the right lateral sling, right hip, anterior chain, thoracic spine, and scapula. Make sure the client shifts over the right foot first before reaching with the left scapula and arm. Remind the client to reach with the scapula, because where the scapula goes, the humerus will follow.

The wall banger shown in Photo 10.2 is essentially a rotational squat designed to mobilize the foot and ankle complex as well as the lateral gluteal complex.

When performing this movement pattern, cue the client to "squish the bug" under the first metatarsal head. This will help mobilize the foot into forefoot abduction, calcaneal eversion, ankle dorsiflexion, and tibial internal rotation. This is a remedial exercise that can be done by nearly all populations.

If the client can control these movements, accelerate to a more progressive strength training plan, with the ultimate goal to return to work, return to sport, and return to life.

PHOTO 10.2 WALL BANGER

## FUNCTIONAL, INTEGRATED MOVEMENT PATTERNS IN THE ACTION PYRAMID

Once a person has the capacity to perform tri-plane integrated movements, the strategy is to use a complementary movement along with a traditional exercise. For example, if the client can do an incline leg press, perhaps couple that with a step-up, an asymmetrical squat, a tri-plane lunging program, or a single-leg squat. The complexity of the pattern you choose should be based on the client's threshold of discomfort, mobility, stability, and quality of movement in the Big Movement Rocks of the foot and ankle complex, hips, and thoracic spine.

If these criteria are successful, it is time to create a comprehensive periodized hybrid program.

# PERIODIZED PROGRAM HYBRID MODELS

Tudor Bompa, a leader in periodization strategies, states:

*"Periodization of strength is structured into phases to maximize sport-specific strength. These phases include muscle endurance, hypertrophy, maximum strength, anatomical adaptation, and reactive training, which incorporate power and explosiveness."*

In his book *Periodization: Training For Sports,* he discusses five basic laws of strength training.

### LAW ONE: DEVELOP JOINT FLEXIBILITY

This coincides with the principle reminding us not to build stability on top of stability. The joints and tissues must have the eccentric loading capability to allow motion from the Big Movement Rocks in three planes of motion. This reduces overuse issues in the regions that require a greater degree of stability. This law is a principle addressed in the function layer of the Action Pyramid.

### LAW TWO: DEVELOP TENDON STRENGTH

Muscle strength is gained more quickly than tendon and ligament strength. Tendons and ligaments adapt through the anatomical adaptation phase of Bompa's model. Without the progressive adaptation of systematic strength training, the connective tissue is at greater risk for injury.

This second law falls in the transition between the function layer to the fitness layer of the pyramid, as it is crucial that the proper motion derives from adequate actions of the Big Movement Rocks. When this is achieved, these tri-plane motions allow soft tissue to efficiently and effectively load with reduced risk of injury.

When conditions are not conducive for proper motion in these regions, not only do compensatory patterns develop, but also the risk of injury to the tendons and ligaments increases, often at compensatory regions as well.

The fitness layer is where we achieve strength gains and anatomical adaptation.

### LAW THREE: DEVELOP CORE STRENGTH

The connotation of the core is always an ongoing and interesting discussion. Most interpretations of the core are of the torso, while some suggest the torso and hips. These ideas are true to an extent. However, the core also includes the extremities, the feet, especially the great toe. Even the skin is part of the core, as all tissue has a fascial connection from top to bottom, side to side, and in-depth when we think three-dimensionally.

Picture an orange and peel it in your mind. The pithy white material connects the rind to the fruit. Now, envision the entire fruit intact. The membrane attaches the slices to one another to hold the slices of fruit together as shown in Photo 10.3.

**PHOTO 10.3 MEMBRANE OF AN ORANGE**

Now, imagine taking a slice of the orange, and notice the membrane enveloping the fruit on the inside. Break open the slice and the individual cells are connected by another membrane.

We can correlate the human body and its fascial attachments to the connectivity of an orange. No matter where in the system of either organism, everything is connected. Based on the movement principles we have discussed throughout this book, to allow optimal function of the central core, the Big Movement Rocks must move freely, yet with stability.

The layers of the Action Pyramid involve core strength, especially on the function and fitness layers.

### LAW FOUR: DEVELOP THE STABILIZERS

In human movement, all muscle and fascial tissue stabilizes joints. As we understand the contemporary research on fascia, we know the skeleton would fall apart without the fascial system.

Bone segments of joints are held in space and position by the fascial system. Bones do not touch under normal, healthy conditions, and when they do, degeneration develops over time.

All movement includes stability. Traditional concepts of stabilizers have commonly referred to the ankle, low back, and shoulder. We want to strengthen the stabilizers by working them in isolated, concentric actions, and often in one plane of motion.

Soon after performing these isolated exercises, you should have your clients do an integrated, tri-plane, eccentrically loaded movement pattern. Often, especially when people have progressed with strength and local tissue endurance, we move to a complementary movement pattern.

For example, if reconditioning a weak or injured rotator cuff of a thrower, you might have the athlete do traditional Jobe and Hughston shoulder stabilizing exercises. These are effective in establishing strength and stability. Dr. Frank Jobe, a well-known pioneer in shoulder surgery, created the Jobe exercises, which include the forward raise, lateral raise, reverse fly, internal rotation, external rotation, empty can, and upward rotation, all designed to improve shoulder stability.

Hughston exercises are performed when lying prone on a table to execute the following shoulder stability movements.

When lying in a prone or face-down position, remember that "upward" is still toward the head as if in a standing position. The fact that the client is in a prone position does not change the direction of movement. The Hughston exercises are performed in the following manner:

*The client will be lying with the thumb pointed toward the head, arm at the side. Instruct the person to lift the arm to 90 degrees abduction to form the letter "T" if possible. Hold for two seconds and then lower the arm to the start position.*

*Lying with the thumb pointed toward the head, the client's arm will be at the side. The person will then lift the arm past 90 degrees abduction to form the letter "Y" if possible. Hold for two seconds and then lower to the start position.*

*Here the client will lie with the palm of the hand flat against the table and the thumb pointed out, and then will lift the arm into extension. Pause for two seconds and then lower.*

*With the elbow bent at 90 degrees and the shoulder abducted to 90 degrees, tell the person to externally rotate the humerus, bringing the hand as high as possible. Pause for two seconds and then lower.*

These are isolated movements, predominantly on one plane of motion, with a concentric contraction done first. After the set or sets of these exercises, you could have the person do an integrated rotator cuff series of patterns in each of the three planes of motion.

Tri-plane rotator cuff patterns are integrated and involve hip action because of how the hip impacts the shoulder girdle in functional movements such as throwing. You will find a listing of our shoulder reconditioning exercises in Appendix Three, page 217.

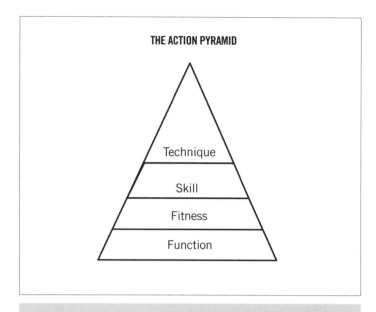

**FIGURE 10.1 THE ACTION PYRAMID**

In this case with a higher-level goal, we use these exercises in the technique layer of the Action Pyramid. However, the preparation for the more dynamic pattern is done in the function and fitness layers.

### LAW FIVE: TRAIN MOVEMENTS, NOT INDIVIDUAL MUSCLES

This concept permeates throughout this book and with those who study human movement. The technique and skill layers of the pyramid scream for this law, as it is here where sport or task specificity requires us to overcome the challenges of gravity, ground-reaction forces, mass, momentum, change of body angles, different surfaces, and various loads under tension.

A single muscle working in isolation accomplishes nothing efficient or effective. The brain and body work through a symphony of motion. In *Muscle Energy Techniques* by Leon Chaitow, Dr. Irwin M. Korr stated:

*"The spinal cord is the keyboard on which the brain plays when it calls for activity. But each 'key' in the console sounds not an individual 'tone' such as the contraction of a particular group of muscle fibers,*

*but a whole 'symphony' of motion…The brain thinks in terms of whole motions, not individual muscles. It calls, selectively, for the preprogrammed patterns in the cord and brain stem, modifying them in countless ways and combining them in an infinite variety in still more complex patterns. Each activity is subject to further modulation refinement, and adjustment by the feedback…from the muscles, tendon, and joints."*

With contemporary research, we can add the fascial system to his description.

## THE MODERN-DAY CONCEPT OF PERIODIZATION

The phases of a comprehensive periodized program include endurance, anatomical adaptation, hypertrophy, maximum strength, power, and reactive training.

These phases can be implemented in a multitude of ways with various training techniques, tools, and scientific study. The success of a well-formulated periodization program is greatly dependent upon the planning of variables such as the load (intensity), number of sets (volume), speed of movement, and rest intervals, among others.

You should definitely consider these factors. However, let's add another extremely important component: *movement variability.*

In the NIH Public Access "The Bliss of Motor Abundance," *Experimental Brain Research*, March, 2012; 217 (1): 1-5, Mark Latash contends:

*"Motor control is an area of natural science exploring how the nervous system interacts with other body parts and the environment to produce purposeful, coordinated actions."*

The article refers to overuse or repetitive patterns as "redundancy," and random patterns as "abundancy." Good variance helps an abundant system manage tasks and unexpected external forces upon the body.

Some of the research has summarized movement variability as "receptions without repletion." It is the random, tri-plane action that creates a motor engram, allowing a person to hone a skill, technique, or task.

The concept of movement variability is a primary objective in the technique and skill layers of the Action Pyramid. When creating a program for a client, we should think beyond the traditional model of classic periodization. Within the fabric of the periodized model, try to blend the Action Pyramid as the foundation on which to plan your goals and objectives.

This foundation is centered around the wants and needs of the client. Weave the Action Pyramid into the classic periodization model, but include the modalities through the use of Dalcourt's Four Quadrant model that intersects movement goals against loaded goals, or what has become known as "loaded movement training."

The 4Q model is a variant of the Four Quadrant model created by Michol Dalcourt of Institute of Motion in Solana Beach, California. Michol is the developer of ViPR™, and is an international presenter with a tremendous understanding of human movement. He also coined the concept of "loaded movement training" based on his observation of linear training, similar to traditional strength training versus three-dimensional training as found in physical efforts such as work in warehouses, on docks, or on the farm.

As Michol states:

*"Loaded movement training combines task-oriented movement patterning with resistance training. Agility and strength come from moving the body in a multitude of purposeful tasks with load, just like back on the farm."*

Using a few of the same concepts on which the idea of Flexibility Highways is based, loaded movement training and functional, integrated training are superior methods of strengthening the fascial system, as these eccentrically load the fascia, load in a tri-plane manner, and remodel the tissue through various angles, paces, and loads.

In the 4Q Model, the y-axis represents the resistance or loads, with low resistance toward the bottom and heavier resistance at the top. The x-axis shows static, uniplanar movement on the left, and movement-based modalities on the right.

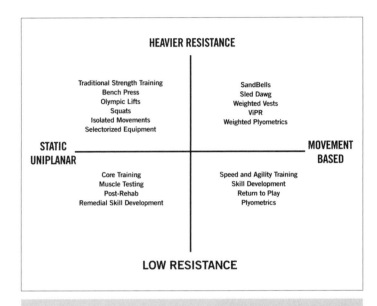

**FIGURE 10.2 THE 4Q MODEL**

Most people you work with will probably start in the lower left quadrant, as this quad represents neuromuscular reeducation, regressive movement patterns to gain both mobility and stability in the Big Movement Rocks, strengthening the weak links in the entire kinetic chain, and gaining core strength. All this will improve coordination, movement efficiency, cardiovascular conditioning, and postural modification for better task development and performance.

Generally speaking, this is a more controlled, often-static activity typically used in subacute rehabilitation, post-rehab, and includes corrective techniques.

The upper-left quadrant, characterized by heavier resistance in a static or uniplane mode, contains the traditional methods of training and is beneficial for gains in muscle hypertrophy, increased strength in muscle, connective tissue, and fascia, stability, and the foundation necessary to build power and explosiveness. This quad usually uses slower movements to improve the tolerance of time under tension. In this quad, you can develop a micro-phase by commencing with a muscle-endurance phase, and then gradually building to the hypertrophy and anatomical-adaptation phases.

The upper-right quadrant represents heavy resistance in a movement-based, tri-plane environment. The objective in this quad is to develop the form and function that leads to the "real life" loads clients, patients, and athletes will face in the lower-right quad.

Modalities most commonly used in this quarter are Sled Dawgs, ViPR™, SandBells®, weighted vests, ActivMotion® Bars, and weighted plyometrics. Using these tools increases strength and explosiveness to meet the challenges people will see in their environments.

Do not expect clients to perform a task at the pace needed in live situations. However, they should become conscious of the proper form, technique, and angles required for the task, occupation, or sport.

In this phase, stop the repetitions if technique or angles are not performed with the precision necessary to produce the greatest efficiency. In this teaching or coaching quadrant, you must be cognizant of the person's style of learning and acceptance of constructive criticism, as precise technical learning starts taking place in this quadrant.

The lower-right quadrant is characterized as tri-plane movement in a lighter-resistance environment. This compartment runs parallel with the skill and technique layers of the Action Pyramid. Pay attention to technique, body and joint angles, and overall form. Attend to the quality of movement in the Big Movement Rocks of the foot and ankle complex, hips, and thoracic spine, so the person can achieve a high level of competency and efficiency.

In this quad, the motor learning from the lower-left quadrant, strength from the upper-left quadrant, and explosive movement variability from the upper-right quadrant all converge to produce the highest possible performance outcome.

This is a hybrid visual of the Action Pyramid, the periodization model, and the 4Q model. The variables can change based on the person's needs and wants, the gait-and-motion analysis, goals, task specificity, or sport. The components of each may vary depending on the tools and equipment you have in your facility.

By no means are any of these written in stone. They should be a living model that changes with the conditions of the client, events the athlete may have on the schedule, the changing of tasks a client must achieve, and any unforeseen event that may transpire. These are just guidelines and are limited only by your creativity.

Program design is an art based on science that should be modulated depending upon the issues at hand.

# CHAPTER ELEVEN

# MOVEMENT TRAINING FOR SPECIAL POPULATIONS

*"The pure and simple is rarely pure and never simple."*

~ OSCAR WILDE

During recent years, there gradually has been a closer relationship between fitness professionals and the physical therapy profession, partly brought on by changes in insurance regulation and reimbursement policies.

As rehabilitation becomes more expensive, insurance carriers raise premiums, deductibles, and reduce amount-of-visit coverage. Physical therapists are often limited in the extent they can treat patients. The primary objective, based on insurance benefits and demands, is commonly restricted to bringing a patient to a point of functional return to daily living. This by no means says the patient is ready to return to the demands of job readiness or sports performance.

Contemporary physical therapy and fitness models blend the two fields, and successful programs have open communication between both sides, allowing feedback from the therapist to the fitness professional and back. Over the course of the emergence of these models, there has been reservation from physical therapists to refer their patients to the general fitness community, and perhaps rightly so.

Our history in fitness brought on this lack of confidence. There has been a lack of consistent competency standards in the fitness field as it relates to understanding movement and exercise programming.

Back in the 1980s when personal training was emerging, if a trainer looked good and had ample muscle tone, it was assumed the person knew the way around a gym. Many "trainers" did exercises that were perceived as circus acts with no regard for a client's health, quality of movement, and history of previous activity.

Fortunately, this is progressively changing as more education organizations provide quality training in client relations, nutrition, biomechanics, gender-related issues, exercise programming, hormonal pathways, and special populations. This is providing a comprehensive integration of skills for trainers. Many trainers have expanded their offerings to encompass those areas of specialization, and are also becoming trained in the psychosocial issues facing their clients, and sometimes even evolving their personal training businesses into life coaching.

Special-population programming includes different applications ranging from injury issues to clients with coronary artery disease, diabetes, weight-control considerations, hypertension, and back pain, to name a few. Program design for special populations must be based on a comprehensive health history, gait-and-motion analysis or a movement screen, psychosocial assessment, and in many cases, medical clearance from a treating physician.

In this section we will address those with low-back pain, and the next chapter will discuss programming for knee problems and shoulder injuries. This is by no means a substitute for medical advice, diagnosis, or physical therapy if warranted. Here we assume the client has been discharged from physical therapy or has been given medical clearance or a referral for fitness programming not requiring physical therapy.

If you doubt that the client should be doing a fitness or special-population exercise program, contact the referring physician for medical clearance and guidelines. Additionally, make sure to communicate the goals, plan, modalities, and exercise methods in writing to the physician.

Equally important, explain the biomechanical approaches and rationale to the doctor. This opens the lines of communication with the medical professional and demonstrates your competence and thought process in assisting the patient.

An IDEA 2013 study by Jan Schroeder, PhD, and Shawn Dolan, PhD, *IDEA Personal Training and Equipment Trends,* confirms the need for personal trainers to raise their competency due to ever-changing client needs. As mentioned earlier, 84% of those who employ a personal trainer have a chronic injury. 35% percent of those participating are seniors, with 16% over 65 years of age, and 25% between ages of 55–64.

The time never has been better to build a fitness or personal training business. But to be successful, you need to address the relationship-building process and understand exercise principles, nutrition, and basic biomechanics to differentiate yourself from other trainers in your area.

## DEVELOPING RELATIONSHIPS

One of the best ways to increase referral business is to develop relationships with local healthcare professionals. Professional disciplines range from family practice doctors, orthopedic specialists, neurosurgeons, podiatric physicians, cardiologists, chiropractors, physical therapists, dietitians, massage therapists, and other healthcare professionals who can be a referral source for you.

Trainers and the professionals listed are not islands unto themselves, but instead are an integrated web of multidisciplinary practices that are part of the healthcare continuum. For example, if you have a client in need of a foot or back evaluation, you should refer out to that specialty. When referring, write a note to the practitioner stating your observations and concerns. The result will be a referral to that professional, and it will raise your image, as it demonstrates your competence when there is a need requiring special attention.

The flipside to this is when the doctor, physical or massage therapist, or chiropractor has a patient requiring fitness training and refers back to you. This professional now has confidence in your abilities, and knows you have a higher level of education, certification, and expertise than trainers who do not.

If your referral to a healthcare professional has merit and some type of intervention is required, not only did you generate revenue for the clinician's practice, but also the client will have benefited and may avoid a potentially serious problem.

Let me give you an example of this, a true situation that happened when I owned a progressive fitness center in the northern suburbs of Chicago. A member who went through school with my wife joined the facility. Each new member at the time received a thorough assessment, including a submaximal bike test to assess hemodynamic response during exercise, a body composition test, and a biomechanical analysis.

This new member had been a football player in high school and still had the high school athlete mentality, only now he was overweight, had borderline high blood pressure, smoked, was sedentary, and ate a high-fat diet.

Due to his multiple risk factors, I advised him I could not do an evaluation other than body composition, and that he could not exercise in our facility until he had a graded exercise stress test with a medical clearance. In those days, I also consulted with a family practice group, and did exercise prescription, nutritional counseling, and graded exercise stress testing. I referred this person to them, and I, along with the chief of medicine in the practice, performed a 12-lead graded exercise stress test on him.

About eight minutes into the test, his blood pressure skyrocketed, his EKG became highly abnormal, and he passed out not once, but twice. We called the paramedics and he was rushed to the hospital, where he also passed out.

After administering medication, and as he awoke, the cardiologist, with whom I had exchanged numerous referrals to and from, was standing over the patient. The potential member said, "I should never have listened to Chuck."

The physician leaned over and said, "Chuck Wolf saved your life!"

The man had a pacemaker implanted, went through cardiac rehab, and finally joined our facility, where he attended regularly. Not only did that member eventually join, but also he became one of our biggest referral sources and advocates.

It is important to have a referral network in the local medical community for the benefit of your clients, as well as to increase your business or that of your facility. Word of mouth is a powerful aspect of building your business. Do not make yourself an island—make yourself part of a chain of islands and the center of a triage network. It will pay dividends.

## SPECIAL POPULATION: LOW-BACK ISSUES

Low-back issues, whether they be back pain or surgery, account for $216 billion globally and more than $90 billion nationally and, in 2016, were the number-two reason people in the United States visited a physician. The majority of these cases stem from a biomechanical problem, although some are genetic.

Dr. Robert Masson, who wrote the foreword to this book, is the leading neurosurgeon in the United States, and quite possibly the world. Formally the medical director of spine surgery for Johnson & Johnson, neurosurgeons from around the world come to learn his advanced techniques in lumbar and cervical spine surgery. Dr. Masson considers spinal injuries as similar to sports injuries, and thinks the approach for treatment of back problems should be addressed accordingly.

He frequently claims that back surgery today resembles ACL surgeries back in the 1970s and '80s. At the time, ACL patients were told to limit activities and advised they would not be able to live life as they had in the past. This is not his philosophy.

His philosophy as a surgeon to the population: Be as fit as possible, do not smoke, eat well, limit alcohol intake, and, if surgery is necessary, get into a prehabilitation program beforehand. Studies have verified if a patient has been in a prehab program, hospital stays are shorter by nearly two days, recovery is quicker, and outcomes are better.

Part of a prehabilitation and rehabilitation program is to perform a gait-and-motion analysis. Generally, those who have back pain, a back injury, or a surgery have common gait limitations, such as limited ankle dorsiflexion, tight thoracic spine resulting in lack of rotation, or tight hip function in all three planes of motion. These issues are to be expected when pain and discomfort are present. However, these limitations are also common when patients are not in pain and appear to be ambulating normally.

Dr. Masson agrees that when ankle dorsiflexion is limited, hip extension will be insufficient. This reduces thoracic rotation to the opposite side, causing more frontal-plane motion in the back, which can result in lumbar facet irritation, disc injury, or both. Additionally, if thoracic spine motion is lacking in the transverse plane, the body will often compensate with increased transverse-plane motion in the lumbar spine.

In the excellent book *Low Back Disorders* by Stuart McGill, PhD, he tells us:

*"The accumulative range of motion at all levels in the transverse plane of the lumbar spine is approximately 13–15 degrees."*

As you already know, the two most mobile regions of the body are the hips and thoracic spine. If motion in the frontal plane is tight in these areas, the body will compensate at the lumbar spine. If this occurs in the transverse plane of the lumbar spine, the risk of injury greatly increases.

When we look at principles and concepts of movement in the lumbar spine, it comes back to the Big Movement Rocks and their ability to amply move with the proper timing in each plane of motion in these regions.

Because back pain is so prevalent, we will use that as our main example of movement training for special populations.

## LOW BACK CONSIDERATIONS AND FUNCTIONAL SOLUTIONS

There are many useful approaches to low-back care, rehabilitation, and post rehabilitation. Many of the movement patterns from one program can carry over to the next, and are not necessarily exclusive to a particular phase of programming. In fact, if a person has progressed to a more advanced phase of back care and then begins to have symptoms, you can still revert to a more regressive plan if it helps with strength or mobility and lessens the discomfort.

The following pages describe an eight-week back reconditioning and strengthening program. It blends traditional exercises with an integrated movement pattern plan designed to address the limitations and compensations found in those with low-back problems.

The goal of the first two weeks is to gain isolated strength in the central unit—the abdominal complex, erector spine, especially of the lumbar region and hip complex.

However, we also want to address the Big Movement Rocks that impact this region, thereby addressing the foot and ankle and thoracic complexes as well. Typically, these regions are immobile. Adhering to the principle to not to build stability on stability, we use three remedial movement patterns: the ankle mobe, wall patterns, and wall bangers.

Additionally, a goal of this first phase is to improve kinesthetic awareness. For those affected with low-back problems, it is very common to have low central-unit strength and lack body awareness in movements. Phase one of our programing is designed with a remedial approach to movement and more isolated, controlled exercises.

The dead bug and supine hip lift emphasize extension and flexion in the sagittal plane without the action of the foot and ankle complex. The thought process is to isolate the tissues in one plane of motion without other possible limiting factors such as lack of foot and ankle function, all to gain the strength and body awareness in the central unit.

As mentioned, a common characteristic of those with low-back pain is limited ankle and foot function. If the ankle is limited in motion, the foot lacks adequate calcaneal eversion and forefoot abduction. Additionally, the tibia will not optimally move into internal rotation. This will cause the hip complex to lose motion in the transverse plane.

The ankle mobe is an important action we use to gain the proper foot and ankle function and to enhance the functional loading of the gluteal complex in all three planes of motion. When this occurs, the rotation of the pelvic girdle will reduce the compensation the lumbar spine produces through the transverse plane.

The next exercise in this phase is the quadruped that incorporates thoracic and hip motion in the transverse plane. This movement pattern isolates the central unit without adding the complexity of the foot and ankle complex and the reaction through the lower extremity. If the client is limited in rotation in the hips and thoracic spine, do not use this exercise. When the motion is poor, rotation may be compensated in the lumbar spine and may be detrimental to the client's progress.

When strength and body awareness improves, you can add wall patterns and wall bangers. These movement patterns include foot and ankle motion as well as the legs, and begin to allow a tri-plane reaction from the feet into the hips. This impacts the lumbar region and thoracic spine during the movements.

The goals and objectives for each phase are noted next.

## PHASE ONE: WEEKS ONE AND TWO

Objectives: *Increase isolated central-unit strength, and kinesthetic awareness*

## SUGGESTED EXERCISES OVERVIEW

- *Dead bug with extremity reach*
- *Supine hip lift*
- *Ankle mobe*
- *Quadruped*
- *Wall patterns*
- *Wall bangers*

# EXERCISE DESCRIPTIONS OF PHASE ONE

Initially, the emphasis of the first two weeks is to gain strength in the sagittal plane.

### DEAD BUG WITH EXTREMITY REACH

The dead bug exercise performed from a supine position is an effective traditional exercise.

Have the client lie face up, with the knees flexed and the feet firmly on the ground. Even though lying supine, cue the person to "Stand tall" from the greater trochanter of the hip through the top of the head, as seen in Photo 11.1. This will place the spine in an optimal position and assist in tissue engagement when executing the exercise.

**PHOTO 11.1 LIE SUPINE IN THE STAND-TALL POSITION**

Next, have the client flex both hips into a 90-degree position. The person will slowly extend one hip until that

leg is three to six inches off the ground while the arms are about 45 degrees abducted and flat on the ground, as shown in Photo 11.2. Then repeat on the opposite side, performing two or three sets of 10 repetitions and build up to 15 repetitions.

**PHOTO 11.2 DEAD BUG WITH HIP EXTENSION**

*Maintain the stand-tall posture even in the supine position.*

If the client can do two or three sets of 10 repetitions without sacrificing form and without discomfort, have the person move an arm into shoulder flexion while maintaining the spinal alignment as shown in Photo 11.3.

**PHOTO 11.3 DEAD BUG WITH SHOULDER FLEXION**

**PHOTO 11.4 DEAD BUG WITH UPPER EXTREMITY REACH**

**PHOTO 11.5 DEAD BUG WITH HIP EXTENSION AND OPPOSITE EXTREMITY REACH**

 *Cue your client to maintain the stand-tall posture throughout this exercise.*

To initiate this movement, have the client hold the spine position while flexing one hip into a 90-degree position, and then return to the start. Then repeat with the other hip.

For the reach, flex the hip and knee to 90 degrees. Separately move each extremity toward the floor—the shoulder moves into flexion; the hips move into extension as shown in Photos 11.3 and 11.4.

Then, have the person move an arm into a shoulder-flexed position until the arm is overhead, or reaches to the client's personal threshold. Have the client do this "around the world" pattern for 10 repetitions per set. Rest about a minute and then repeat in the opposite direction.

If well tolerated, cue the person to move the opposite arm and hip into the same respective positions while keeping the spine neutral as demonstrated in Photo 11.5.

Assuming the person can do this with good form and no discomfort, the second phase of this exercise is to simultaneously perform the same lifts of each extremity while moving the opposite arm and leg.

When a person is weak in the dead bug, it is a common compensation to extend the lumbar spine or rotate away from the weak extremity. Form is critically important and must be maintained. If the person cannot keep proper form, do not progress levels or repetitions until you observe good form.

Start with five to 10 repetitions in the same direction and then repeat in the opposite direction.

### SUPINE HIP LIFT (BRIDGING)

This exercise is extremely effective for improving low-back strength in the sagittal plane. Have the client lie in the stand-tall position and cue to "Stand tall," meaning lie tall. Keep the feet flat on the floor and place the arms about 45 degrees abducted from the sides.

Keeping the central unit aligned, have the client lift the hips as high as possible, as seen in Photo 11.6, but not to the point of hyperextension in the lumbar spine. Remind the person to lift the hips and low back as one unit, not segmentally.

**PHOTO 11.6 SAGITTAL-PLANE HIP LIFT**

Repeat this pattern for five to 10 repetitions, depending upon tolerance and threshold. Perform two or three sets, and gradually build up to three sets of 20 reps over two weeks if possible.

## ANKLE MOBE

The ankle mobe is designed to gain motion through the talocrural joint in the sagittal plane, the subtalar joint in the frontal plane, help with tibial internal rotation in the transverse plane, and forefoot abduction in the frontal plane or transverse axis of the foot.

If any one of these movements is limited, the entire reaction through the foot and ankle complex is compromised and will create compensation through the kinetic chain.

Invariably, nearly all patients with low-back discomfort have foot and ankle limitations to some degree. Whichever component is limited, the body must gain mobility elsewhere to allow adequate motion in the body. We use the ankle mobe to help regain foot and ankle mobility to reduce those compensations.

The ankle mobe is performed by placing a foot on a six- or eight-inch box, as shown in Photo 11.7. The trail leg is extended with the foot pointed forward. Have the client imagine there is a rope around the hips pulling the hips forward.

**PHOTO 11.7 ANKLE MOBE START POSITION**

Tell the person to drive the forward knee over the foot, but not to the point the heel lifts off the ground, as shown in Photo 11.8. This will cause the tibia to move over the foot, resulting in ankle dorsiflexion.

Here we are addressing both ankle complexes during the gait cycle—the forward foot through the mid-stance phase, and the rear ankle as it would be just prior to heel-off.

**PHOTO 11.8 ANKLE MOBE WITH ANKLE DORSIFLEXED**

**PHOTO 11.9 ANKLE MOBE WITH ANTERIOR REACH**

To modify the effect of the ankle mobe, the person can drive the hips side to side in the frontal plane with the hands forward in a bilateral reach, as seen in Photo 11.9. This will help mobilize the frontal-plane motion of the subtalar joint in eversion and inversion, and at the same time impact hips in adduction and abduction. Likewise, it will help gain movement through the forefoot as well.

To gain further ankle mobility and hip extension, we do this movement with shoulder flexion of the arm on the same side as the extended hip, as shown in Photo 11.10. This is an overhead reach while driving the hips forward to gain sagittal-plane motion of the hip and ankle joints.

Exercise caution if the client has significant lordosis of the lumbar spine. Make sure the person does not hyperextend through the lumbar spine, but rather extends through the hip.

**PHOTO 11.10 ANKLE MOBE WITH SHOULDER FLEXION ARM REACH**

**PHOTO 11.11 ANKLE MOBE WITH BILATERAL ARM REACH**

Photo 11.11 demonstrates the ankle mobe with a bilateral arm reach in the frontal plane to the opposite side of the forward leg. This can also be done with a bilateral arm reach to the same side of the lead leg. The movement causes internal rotation of the same-side hip, femoral internal rotation, tibial internal rotation, calcaneal eversion, and forefoot abduction.

*Make sure the knee of the lead leg is over the shoelaces of the front foot. This causes ankle dorsiflexion of both ankles. Have the person rock back and forth to mobilize the calf group and ankle joints, and then drive the hips side to side to gain frontal-plane motion of the hips, midfoot, and subtalar joint.*

This can also be done with a bilateral arm reach to the same side of the lead leg. This option causes internal rotation of the same-side hip, femoral external rotation, tibial external rotation, calcaneal inversion, and forefoot adduction as demonstrated in Photo 11.12.

**PHOTO 11.12 ANKLE MOBE WITH SAME-SIDE BILATERAL ARM REACH**

Both of these movements will create internal hip rotation; however, the real motion of the femur is different. As in Photo 11.11, the opposite or contralateral reach will cause the femur to medially rotate farther than the ilium. Based on the principle of the distal bone in relation to the proximal bone, this results in internal hip rotation. Moving downward, the tibia will rotate medially, the calcaneus will evert, and the forefoot will abduct.

In Photo 11.12, the same-side ipsilateral reach will turn the torso laterally and "carry" the ilium with it. The ilium moves farther toward lateral rotation and is in a position that places the femur into a relative medial position to the ilium, resulting in internal hip rotation. In both cases, the hip is in relative internal rotation.

However, in Photo 11.12, the femur moves laterally, the tibia follows into external rotation as compared to Photo

11.11. The calcaneus is relatively inverted, and the forefoot is adducted. Try moving into these positions yourself and feel the motion that results in mobilization of the ankle.

Both of these reaches and reactions enhance the mobility of the ankle in dorsiflexion and the subtalar joint in eversion and inversion.

These movements can be performed with or without a box.

### QUADRUPED

The primary purpose of the quadruped exercise is to gain mobility in the thoracic spine and hips in a controlled, remedial environment.

The client begins on hands and knees. Make sure the hands are directly under the shoulders and the knees are under the hips as seen in Photo 11.13. For comfort, make sure the client can tolerate this position.

**PHOTO 11.13 QUADRUPED START POSITION**

Have the person maintain the stand-tall position for spine stability, and cue to reach with the left scapula under the right arm, as seen in Photo 11.14. Remember, where the scapula goes, the humerus will follow.

**PHOTO 11.14 QUADRUPED WITH ARM REACH**

The goal of this is to gain thoracic rotation to the right, as well as right shoulder stability and core strength.

Repeat the same movement with the right arm reaching to the left.

Next, have the client drive the left knee to the right, moving it under the right hip, as shown in Photo 11.15. This will help with stability and mobility of the left hip complex, and mobility of the right hip region as well. Repeat on the opposite side.

**PHOTO 11.15 QUADRUPED WITH HIP ROTATION**

If the person does not have the mobility in the hips or the ability to stabilize the spine during this activity, do not use the quadruped exercise until these areas become more mobile or stronger. If the client can do this, start with five reps using each limb and progress to 20 repetitions for three sets.

As the client progresses with minimal or no discomfort and no form breakdown, move to the more complex movements such as wall patterns and wall bangers.

### WALL PATTERNS

Wall patterns are a safe and controlled motion that will help mobilize the foot and ankle complex, hips, and thoracic spine. Have your client stand at arm's length away from a wall with the hands against the wall at shoulder height as seen in Photo 11.16.

**PHOTO 11.16 WALL PATTERNS START POSITION**

Next, imagine a clock on the wall with 12:00 and 6:00 representing the sagittal plane, 3:00 and 9:00 as the frontal plane.

With the heels remaining on the ground, have the client extend through the hips while reaching upward toward the 12:00 o'clock position as viewed in Photo 11.17. Make sure the motion is captured through the ankles when moving through ankle dorsiflexion and the hips extend, then return to the start position.

This action will improve motion along the Anterior Flexibility Highway.

**PHOTO 11.17 WALL PATTERNS WITH A REACH TO THE 12:00 O'CLOCK POSITION**

**PHOTO 11.18 WALL PATTERNS WITH A REACH TO THE 6:00 O'CLOCK POSITION**

Next, as shown in Photo 11.18, have the client squat and reach to the 6:00 o'clock position while maintaining the stand-tall posture. It is important to achieve ankle dorsiflexion and to have the hips move into a relative anterior pelvic tilt during the squat, reach, and return to the starting position.

This movement will improve action along the Posterior Flexibility Highway.

Now have the client shift the hips to the right and reach to the 3:00 o'clock position. It is important to think about doing this from the bottom up so the hips will align over the feet. If it is done top down, the shoulders and thoracic spine will move into lateral flexion and may cause problems in the thoracic or lumbar spine. The correct motion is viewed in Photo 11.19.

**PHOTO 11.19 WALL PATTERNS WITH A REACH TO THE 3:00 O'CLOCK POSITION**

**PHOTO 11.20 WALL PATTERNS OPPOSITE LATERAL REACH**

Repeat with the same alignment of the hip over the foot to the left while reaching to the 9:00 o'clock position. This action will eccentrically load the lateral gluteal complex and improve movement side to side along the Lateral Flexibility Highway.

Do not think that 12 to 6 o'clock is only for the right-sided motions and 6 to 12 o'clock is only for the left. Reach to the opposite side, as seen in Photo 11.20. This will not only improve opposite lateral reach, but will compel transverse-plane motion as well.

This motion will enhance movement in the Lateral and Posterior X-Factor Flexibility Highways.

Start these movements at shoulder height and then add the vertical angulations to get more sagittal-plane loading through the system as seen in Photo 11.21.

**PHOTO 11.21 WALL PATTERNS 3 O'CLOCK POSITION AT WAIST HEIGHT**

Notice the position of the hands and arms in the photos. As the client starts at the waist- or hip-height positions, there will be more loading into the system in the sagittal plane. This will help mobilize and strengthen the tissues.

Begin with three repetitions in each direction and progress to five to 10 reps for two or three sets.

## WALL BANGERS

Essentially, wall bangers are a rotational squat performed in a safe, controlled environment. The goal of this pattern is to gain mobility in the Big Movement Rocks while building eccentric strength and loading. As the client reaches during the squatting action, the hip will adduct and bang against the wall as shown in Photo 11.22.

PHOTO 11.22 WALL BANGERS

With the wall on the side of the client, cue to "Stand tall. Shine the Beacon of Life toward the foot away from the wall."

The client should perform a rotational squat while reaching away with both arms at chest or waist height.

Make sure the motion is coming from the foot and ankle complex and the hips.

If the client reports a mild discomfort in the knee closest to the wall, turn that foot inward about five degrees, which should reduce that problem. When the hips become more mobile, gradually move the foot position back toward a neutral foot placement.

Repeat for five to 10 repetitions.

If the person has progressed with minimal or no discomfort or form breakdown, you should move to the second phase of this program.

## PROCEEDING TO PHASE TWO

Once the client demonstrates greater strength through increased repetitions and sets with minimal or no discomfort in Phase One, it is time to progress to Phase Two. Phase One is designed to gain strength primarily in the sagittal plane, while Phase Two targets improving movement in the frontal and transverse planes.

As you read in the *Preprogramming Insights* chapter beginning on page 137, we need to gain motion in the frontal plane prior to attempting to gain it in the transverse plane. This means to start with the supine hip lift in the frontal plane before doing it in the transverse plane. There must be good hip mobility in the frontal plane to be able to perform the supine hip lift in the transverse plane.

The core stabilization with step-out works in the frontal plane before attempting to do the core stabilization with a rotational step-out in the transverse plane.

The pivotal toe touches will improve mobility in the foot and ankle complex by emphasizing ankle dorsiflexion, tibial internal rotation, calcaneal eversion, and forefoot abduction.

Level One warding patterns begin to incorporate full-body reactions in three planes of motion as we apply external forces.

## PHASE TWO: WEEKS THREE AND FOUR

*May start at week two if the patient has progressed and tolerated Phase One well*

*Objectives: Gain frontal- and transverse-plane motion, and mobilize foot and ankle and hip complexes through movement patterns*

### SUGGESTED EXERCISES OVERVIEW

- *Supine hip lift—frontal plane*
- *Supine hip lift—transverse plane if there is good mobility in the hip complex*
- *Core stabilization with step-out*
- *Pivotal toe touches*
- *Level One warding patterns with a partner*

## EXERCISE DESCRIPTIONS OF PHASE TWO

Initially, the emphasis of the second two weeks is increased mobility in the frontal and transverse planes.

### SUPINE HIP LIFT

If the client has tolerated the supine hip lift as seen earlier in Photo 11.6 without discomfort and performs it in good form, try doing it as a frontal-plane lift. The initial movement is the same as the sagittal-plane hip lift. Then, from the hips-up position, have the person "step out" toward the side—abducting the hip, but having the hip follow the leg to the side as seen in Photo 11.23. This will load the hip, lumbar spine, and abdominal complex in the frontal plane.

**PHOTO 11.23 FRONTAL-PLANE HIP LIFT**

Repeat this pattern for five to 10 repetitions, depending upon tolerance and threshold. Perform two or three sets, and gradually build up to three sets of 20 reps over two weeks if possible.

If the client has tolerated the frontal-plane hip lift well and without discomfort, try the transverse-plane hip lift, as seen in Photo 11.24.

**PHOTO 11.24 TRANSVERSE-PLANE HIP LIFT**

Before attempting this exercise, there must be a good range of motion of the hips and lower thoracic spine in the transverse plane.

Repeat this pattern for five to 10 repetitions, depending on tolerance and threshold. Perform two or three sets, and gradually build up to three sets of 20 reps over two weeks if possible.

### CORE STABILIZATION WITH STEP-OUT

The core stabilization with step-out targets the abdominal complex, especially the obliques. This movement is executed with a band, tubing, or a cable system. While standing with the equipment to the side, have the person stand tall and hold the handle directly at the midline. The elbows should be extended, yet soft and not firmly locked.

Tell the client to step toward the opposite side from where the implement is attached, moving into a side lunge as shown in Photo 11.25.

**PHOTO 11.25 CORE STABILIZATION WITH STEP-OUT USING A BAND**

When stepping to the side, the person will feel tension through the obliques. At the finish of the side lunge, look for ankle dorsiflexion, and see that the knee and hip are slightly flexed, similar to an athletic power position.

Upon returning to the starting position, the client must control the return action and not let the resistance pull the body back. Have the person do this movement 10 times for two or three sets, alternating sides.

When the client is able to improve frontal-plane motion of the hips, along with gaining abdominal and back strength, you can progress to incorporating a rotation in the movement. This means doing the step-out, and then rotating into the lunging hip, shown in Photo 11.26.

**PHOTO 11.26 CORE STABILIZATION WITH STEP-OUT PLUS ROTATION**

It is important to keep the hip over the foot of the lunging side to maintain hip adduction, which will enhance hip rotation on the same side. For ample hip rotation, there must be good range of motion in the frontal plane.

### PIVOTAL TOE TOUCH

The pivotal toe touch mobilizes the foot and ankle complex in three planes of motion. This mobility is essential for optimal movement through the entire chain. It is easily administered, and the client can execute it anywhere and anytime.

Have the person stand in a bilateral or neutral foot position. If the left foot and ankle need mobilization, shift the weight over the left foot. It is acceptable to hold or balance on a stable fixture, such as a counter or desktop.

**PHOTO 11.27 A AND B PIVOTAL TOE TOUCH
TO THE 4:00 O'CLOCK AND 10:00 O'CLOCK POSITIONS**

Tell the person to imagine standing in the middle of a clock, and then to rotate toward 3:00 or 4:00 o'clock. Cue to "Shine the Beacon of Life" when rotating—as the pelvis goes, the low back will follow.

Once reaching the person's rotational threshold, cue to do a mini-squat to load the system. When rotating toward the right, the calcaneus will evert, the tibia will rotate to the right, the ankle to move into a relative dorsiflexed position, and the forefoot will abduct.

Next, have the person rotate toward the left to approximately the 10:00 or 11:00 o'clock position. When rotating to the left, the calcaneus will invert, the tibia will rotate toward the left, the ankle will go into a relative plantar-flexed position, and the forefoot will adduct. Once the client reaches this threshold, ask the person to perform a mini-squat.

Remind the client to keep the big toe joint firmly on the ground. This impacts the rest of the body and will improve foot and ankle function and help gain mobility through the hips.

### WARDING PATTERNS

"Warding" means to guard or protect, such as warding off external forces. When forces are exerted on the body, they must be mitigated and absorbed to protect against the invading energy. The body must be strong enough to absorb the forces, especially needing stability in the central unit.

Additionally, the Big Movement Rocks must have the mobility to allow shock absorption, or a wave of force will be sent into the body, causing an increased risk of injury, especially to the low back. Warding patterns are an effective method to gain this type of strength in the central unit, back, shoulders, hips, and legs.

To perform this exercise, have the client establish a strong power base by standing with the feet slightly wider than the hips, ankles dorsiflexed about 45 degrees, and knees and hips flexed approximately 80–90 degrees. The person should be in the stand-tall position from the greater trochanter through the spine to the top of the head.

Next, have the person flex the shoulder at shoulder height and place the palms of the hands together. Facing the client, apply force into the hands side to side as shown in Photo 11.28. This affects the frontal plane from the top down and bottom up, impacting the sagittal plane, and on angles, causing a transverse-plane reaction.

**PHOTO 11.28 WARDING PATTERN LEVEL ONE—
OBSERVE THE POWER POSITIONS**

This can be adapted for all populations by modulating the amount of force exerted, by changing to asymmetrical foot positions as shown in Photo 11.29, and by adding proprioceptive input such as shaking the head, closing one or both eyes, or a combination of these.

**PHOTO 11.29 WARDING PATTERN LEVEL ONE, ASYMMETRICAL STANCE**

It will be more challenging to resist force when it is applied toward the rear leg. This is because the hip and gluteal complex are not in an optimal position to resist the applied force.

If the person has progressed with minimal or no discomfort or form breakdown, move to the next phase of the program.

## PROCEEDING TO PHASE THREE

This stage challenges the client with more stabilization requirements.

Level Two warding patterns with a stability ball accomplish a couple of objectives. Besides gaining integrated core strength, holding the stability ball also recruits the arms, latissimus dorsi, hips, and legs to ward off the external forces while holding an object.

The crossover walk eccentrically loads the Anterior X-Factor of the Flexibility Highway system from the opposite adductor group to the obliques through the opposite pectoral region and shoulders. The Anterior X-Factor improves the range of motion with rotation and extension.

When working with your client on the crossover walk, start with the Anterior X-Factor because there is less relative rotation than the Posterior X-Factor. Therefore, before implementing the Posterior X-Factor, gain movement in the opposing Anterior X-Factor.

The exercises with the TRX® or other suspension training system build integrated core strength while implementing a stable environment throughout the system.

Progress to the next phase in weeks five and six, assuming the person has the strength gains necessary to perform higher-level activities without back pain.

### PHASE THREE: WEEKS FIVE AND SIX

*May start at week five if the patient has progressed and tolerated Stages One and Two well*

Objectives: *Increase tri-plane motion in the hips and thoracic spine, and gain integrated strength*

### SUGGESTED EXERCISE OVERVIEW

- *Level Two warding patterns with a stability ball*
- *Crossover walk, Anterior X-Factor*
- *TRX® chest press*
- *TRX® lat pull*

## EXERCISE DESCRIPTIONS OF PHASE TWO

Initially, the emphasis of this phase is integrated strength and stabilization.

### WARDING PATTERNS

In weeks five and six, you will progress the warding patterns to a second level that includes holding a stability ball, as seen in Photos 11.30 and 11.31. The concepts and variations are the same as the Level One warding patterns, but done while holding a stability ball. If the client is having difficulty progressing from the basic warding pattern, do not progress to Level Two.

**PHOTO 11.30 WARDING PATTERN LEVEL TWO, BILATERAL STANCE**

**PHOTO 11.31 WARDING PATTERN LEVEL TWO, ASYMMETRICAL STANCE**

The stability ball adds more arm integration that recruits the latissimus dorsi and arm musculature. Additionally, the positioning of the body while holding the stability ball increases the hoop tension, which is the force exerted circumferentially around the inner cylinder of the torso. This consists of the abdominal, obliques, intercostals, erector spinae, multifidus, psoas, iliacus, diaphragm ribs, and pelvis. The combination of hoop tension and intra-abdominal pressure help to increase low-back strength.

### CROSSOVER WALK

The crossover walk adds to the development of dynamic stability in the central unit during single leg–stance phase, as well as during changes of body angles. At this point in the progression, it is necessary to begin more dynamic movements to control, transfer, and mitigate forces through the body during variable movement patterns.

To appreciate the crossover walk, we need to review the Anterior and Posterior X-Factors of the Flexibility Highways, covered beginning on page 103. The Anterior X-Factor incorporates the hip flexors and adductors of the opposite hip, into the abdominal complex and obliques, to the opposite pectoral complex, and into the shoulder. If there is good range of motion in the Anterior X-Factor, it will enhance extension and rotation to the opposite side.

The Posterior X-Factor runs from the opposite gluteal region, through the lumbar fascia, into the opposite latissimus dorsi to the posterior shoulder. When there is good range of motion in the Posterior X-Factor, we gain flexion and rotation.

Both of the X-factors of the Flexibility Highways are critical for increased motion of the hips and thoracic spine to reduce stress and transverse motion in the lumbar spine.

To begin the crossover walk, place low hurdles in a zigzag pattern at 90-degree angles to each other—see Photo 11.32. If hurdles are not available or are too high, use tape on the floor in the same configuration.

**PHOTO 11.32 HURDLE SET-UP FOR CROSSOVER WALK**

**PHOTO 11.33 ANTERIOR X-FACTOR CROSSOVER WALK**

Start from the stand-tall position. As seen in Photo 11.33, the person will step over the hurdle with the right foot, then shift bodyweight toward the right foot while reaching with both arms back to the left foot. Make sure the client does not flex at the hips, but rather has the hip extended and under the torso.

Next, the person will step with the left leg up to the right, and try to pause while standing on only the right leg, as in Photo 11.34.

**PHOTO 11.34 CROSSOVER WALK, MID-STANCE**

Tell the person to stand tall and stride with the left leg toward the left at a perpendicular angle to the right leg. The weight shifts into the left leg while reaching back toward the right leg as shown in Photo 11.35. This will build stability and stretch the right adductors.

Continue this pattern through the remainder of the hurdles. We usually set up four or five hurdles, but that will depend on your equipment.

**PHOTO 11.35 ANTERIOR X-FACTOR CROSSOVER WALK**

Make note of the shift into the lead leg to stretch the adductors. Start with this pattern, as it does not require as much rotational movement through the hips and thoracic spine. Notice the right adductors are lengthened in Photo 11.35 versus in Photo 11.33, where the left adductors are being stretched and movement is toward the right side.

If the client is progressing without difficulty or discomfort, move to the next phase in weeks seven and eight.

The criteria we follow to begin to return to play is good quality of motion in the Big Movement Rocks of the foot and ankle complex, hips, and thoracic spine, without any compensatory motions, no back pain, and no radicular pain in the extremities.

Usually, the Posterior X-Factor work is added in this next phase if the client has sufficient range of motion through the Anterior X-Factor.

### PHASE FOUR: WEEKS SEVEN AND EIGHT
*May start earlier if previous stages are well tolerated*

Objectives: *Increase range of motion in the transverse plane of the hips and thoracic spine, and start activities for return to work and play*

Phase Four prepares the client for return to work or play. The Posterior X-Factor is implemented here if the client has sufficient range of motion in the Anterior X-Factor without any undue discomfort.

Movement patterns requiring more stabilization are blended into the program along with more dynamic tri-plane activities.

### SUGGESTED EXERCISE OVERVIEW
- *Crossover walk with Posterior X-Factor if there is good motion in the hips and thoracic spine*
- *TRX® single-leg stabilization*
- *TRX® warding patterns if there is good strength in the shoulder girdle and central unit and no back pain*
- *Tri-plane lunges with reaches*
- *Tri-plane activities*

## EXERCISE DESCRIPTIONS OF PHASE FOUR

Initially, the emphasis of the final phase is increased range of transverse-plane motion in the hips and thoracic spine.

### CROSSOVER WALK WITH POSTERIOR X-FACTOR
As the client establishes improved mobility in the hips and thoracic spine, you can commence the Posterior X-Factor pattern. The posterior pattern requires more motion in the transverse plane, hence the need for ample mobility in the hips and thoracic spine. You should normally wait to use this pattern until Phase Four; however, it is up to you to determine when the client is ready.

The person would begin by stepping over the hurdle with the left foot forward, shift bodyweight onto the left leg, and reach with both arms toward the left.

**PHOTO 11.36 POSTERIOR X-FACTOR CROSSOVER WALK**

It is imperative to use the cues of "Stand tall," "Shine the Beacon of Life into the lead leg," and "Reach with the scapula." If these cues are not followed and the client is limited in movement in the Big Movement Rocks, the rotation can go through the lumbar spine and beyond the person's low-back mobility threshold.

The person will then step with the right leg into a neutral position next to the left leg as shown in Photo 11.37.

Ideally, have the client stand in a single-leg stance at this point. However, if the person loses balance, the right foot can be on the ground to stabilize.

**PHOTO 11.37 POSTERIOR X-FACTOR CROSSOVER WALK, MID-STANCE**

Have the person lead with the right leg crossing over the hurdle to land. When moving into this position, both arms reach to the right, as seen in Photo 11.38.

Note the rotation into the lead leg, shining the Beacon of Life, and reaching with the scapula.

**PHOTO 11.38 POSTERIOR X-FACTOR CROSSOVER WALK**

Continue this pattern through the remainder of the hurdles. This movement pattern will gain range of motion on the posterior side from the opposite hip to the opposite shoulder complex.

We usually set up four or five hurdles, but your setup will depend upon how many hurdles you have.

## SUSPENSION TRAINERS

The use of suspension trainers such as the TRX® is a staple in our back reconditioning and strengthening programs. When using this equipment, we can vary the resistance by changing the angles of the body. It is important to maintain the tall position when using a suspension trainer, as this will engage the central unit.

Have the person perform a TRX® lat pull, seen in Photos 11.39A and B, and a TRX® chest press seen in Photos

11.40A and B, doing anywhere between eight and 15 repetitions, depending on the person's initial conditioning. The goal is three sets of 15–20 reps of each exercise.

**PHOTOS 11.39 A AND B TRX® LAT PULL START AND FINISH**

**PHOTOS 11.40 A AND B TRX® CHEST PRESS**

When the client is successful with the double-leg stance, try working in a single-leg stance with no resistance as viewed in Photo 11.41. It is important to have good range of motion and stability in the ankle and hip to do this pattern.

**PHOTO 11.41 TRX® SINGLE-LEG BALANCE**

Remind the client to maintain the stand-tall position. Hold this for 10 to 30 seconds for three to five repetitions.

To begin, have the client stand tall, with both feet on the ground, and place the handles in an anterior overhead reach while leaning forward from the ankles. It is important to have good ankle dorsiflexion, good mobility in the hip flexors, ample stability and mobility in the shoulder girdle, and good central-unit strength. Hold this position for 10–30 seconds, and repeat five to 10 repetitions in each set. Repeat for two or three sets, depending upon the client's threshold.

Once the person is competent with this pattern, try it from a single-leg stance, but weigh the risk-to-reward benefits beforehand. If the client is an athlete or a strong person with good central-unit strength, it may be feasible to use this drill. However, if the person has been sedentary, possesses other injury issues, is a senior, or has an overall low-activity lifestyle, do not use this movement pattern.

### WARDING PATTERNS

Warding patterns were introduced into the back reconditioning program in Phase Two and we used a more advanced version using a stability ball in Phase Three. This is the third level to the warding pattern series described on page 185, and is performed similarly to the TRX® single-leg stabilization.

Before commencing any warding patterns with a suspension trainer, have the client perform a double-leg stance using the TRX® or similar suspension trainer. This will develop the integrated core strength while having the assistance of holding on to an unstable device such as the handles of the TRX®.

Have the client hold this position for 15 seconds and rest for 10 to 20 seconds. If successful in maintaining stability, increase the holding phase to 30–60 seconds, depending upon the person's strength. When the client can perform this movement three times, implement resistance by applying forces through the handles.

Following the TRX® single-leg stabilization exercise, begin applying forces through the handles as shown in Photos 11.42 and 11.43. Make sure the client has strength in the shoulder girdle complex to resist the force while holding the position.

**PHOTO 11.42 WARDING PATTERN LEVEL THREE, BILATERAL STANCE**

Apply force in three planes of motion in an up-and-down pattern to recruit the tissue in the sagittal plane, in a side-to-side manner, which will impact the frontal plane, and in diagonal patterns to affect the tissue in the transverse plane.

This is an effective integrated movement pattern. However, it can be troublesome if you apply too much force. Keep in mind you are trying to offer a challenge, not beat the client. This is not a contest of who can last the longest; rather, it is an assistive technique to help the person "ward off" external forces and to maintain balance during the application of force.

Exercise caution if the client has a history of pain or discomfort in the upper back or shoulder region. Also, make sure the person does not experience any low-back pain or hyperextension in the lumbar area. If this occurs, correct this form by cuing to maintain the stand-tall posture. If the discomfort persists, cease this activity.

Photo 11.43 shows the TRX® warding pattern in a single-leg stance. When in a single-leg stance, there are three points of contact: both hands and one leg. When in these stances, the tension on all tissues is greater due to the increasingly unstable environment.

It is very important the client is able to control this posture before attempting this movement pattern. If a person experiences any discomfort, cease this movement and revert back to the bilateral stance when doing TRX® warding patterns.

### TRI-PLANE LUNGES

Tri-plane lunges are the foundation for hip mobility in three planes of motion. These lead to excellent loading and help enable strength gains for all walks of life.

In this phase of reconditioning from back disorders, begin the lunging program only if the person has good motion in the Big Movement Rocks and is able to control the movement without significant wobbling, instability, or other compensations.

The dynamics of tri-plane lunges can begin with a shorter stride in each plane, and then gradually increasing the movement when the client gains strength, mobility, efficiency, and confidence.

Imagine the person is standing in the middle of a clock with 12:00 o'clock to the front. This is a lunge in the sagittal plane, as seen in Photos 11.44 A and B.

**PHOTOS 11.44 A AND B TWO VIEWS OF A SAGITTAL-PLANE LUNGE**

The frontal plane is represented at the 3:00 and 9:00 o'clock positions as shown in Photos 11.45 and 11.46.

**PHOTO 11.43 WARDING PATTERN LEVEL THREE, SINGLE-LEG STANCE**

**PHOTO 11.45 FRONTAL-PLANE LUNGE WITH INTERNAL HIP ROTATION**

**PHOTO 11.46 FRONTAL-PLANE LUNGE WITH EXTERNAL HIP ROTATION**

*Notice the ankle dorsiflexion, tibial internal rotation, and hip adduction versus with the hip in external rotation, and with less ankle dorsiflexion, and hip abduction. Both positions will eccentrically load the adductors and are necessary for mobility and strength, especially for active populations.*

You will initially work in the sagittal and frontal planes, as these are more linear and typically easier to control. If the client can tolerate frontal-plane lunges, shown in Photos 11.45 and 11.46, perform two variations, a lunge that finishes with the hip over the knee and toe, and the other with the foot facing either the 3:00 or 9:00 o'clock positions as shown in Photo 11.46.

The difference between the two variations is that the position with the hip over the knee and the knee over the foot creates greater internal rotation of the hip as seen earlier in Photo 11.45. Here the hip is flexed and adducted, resulting in more relative internal rotation, versus the foot facing the positions seen in Photo 11.46.

In both variations, the adductors are eccentrically loaded and both lengthen and strengthen these structures, contributing to greater hip mobility in all three planes of motion.

The transverse plane is a rotational lunge moving into the 4:00 and 8:00 o'clock positions. The key to this movement pattern is to open the hips into external rotation before lunging. View Photo 11.47 and notice how the left foot is pointed to the 8:00 o'clock position and the right foot remains pointed toward the 12:00 o'clock position.

**PHOTO 11.47 TRANSVERSE-PLANE LUNGE TO THE 8:00 O'CLOCK POSITION**

If both feet were rotated toward the 8:00 o'clock position, it essentially would be a sagittal-plane lunge.

If the client is lacking mobility in the gluteal or adductor complexes, do not begin work in this plane of motion until achieving better mobility.

Start with three to five repetitions and build up to 10 reps each side, adding one rep each workout. If the client develops tightness in the adductor region, do not add repetitions, as this is due to adductor weakness during the eccentric load. When this happens, it usually occurs after doing too many frontal-plane lunges.

Start this program by alternating each leg in each direction, lunging with the right leg, then lunging with the left leg. This is called an alternating sequence.

When the client can achieve two sets of 10 repetitions in each direction in the alternating sequence, do one lunge in each direction with the same leg, and then repeat the same pattern with the other leg.

When starting this sequence, lower the number of repetitions back to five, and build the number of repetitions up again. The reason for this is there is less rest between repetitions and it is more challenging than the alternating sequence. This is called unilateral alternating.

When the client can perform two sets of 10 repetitions of unilateral alternating lunges, go back down to five repetitions, doing all five reps in succession with the same leg. Build this up to 10 repetitions each leg. This is called the unilateral sequence.

## AND, FINALLY, THE RETURN-TO-PLAY PHASE

The return-to-play phase of rehab is an exciting time for most people. They recognize they are making progress and can begin to reidentify with a favored sport or desired activities of daily living. Even though we are using the phrase "return to play," this can also include activities similar to labor, hobbies, or lifestyle goals…not just sport. This phase is an open forum to use creativity and implement various tools of the trade your client may use in sport or life.

For example, I once worked with a professional tennis player who had a micro discectomy. In her recovery phase, we used the same progressions as outlined in the back rehabilitation plan just described.

When we started the return-to-play stage, we began with a tri-plane lunging program with arm reaches in various directions. As she became proficient with these movements and had good action in her Big Movement Rocks, she did the same movements as I rolled tennis balls toward her and she fielded them and tossed back to me. All of a sudden, I saw a smile and heard laughter, as this was not a rehab exercise anymore, but rather something she could relate to and could envision in a competitive environment.

She started with three repetitions of four lunge variations encompassing all three planes of motion. As she gained strength, mobility, and endurance, she gradually increased to three sets of 10 reps, and she truly enjoyed the competitive moments. Not only did she do the various lunges, we modified them by increasing the speed and distance she had to cover to field the tennis balls, all while she regained athletic coordination.

The last component to this strategy was to give her a tennis racquet to hold or hit the balls back while executing the same movement patterns.

The return-to-play phase may be the final stage of a rehab program; however, it goes well beyond just the aspects of strength and rehab. It gives the client the motivation, confidence, and drive to continue with the conditioning after discharge and while moving back toward the field of play, whether that be sport, work, a hobby, or life chores.

To summarize the progressions of this sample back reconditioning program, we use guidelines of progression. These are based on the tolerance and symptoms of the client, the quality of movement through the Big Movement Rocks, and the person's strength and stability during the exercises.

In the next chapter, we will expand on these programming ideas to cover knee and shoulder joint issues.

CHAPTER TWELVE

# PROGRAMMING AROUND JOINT ISSUES

*"Look deep into nature, and then you will
understand everything better."*

~ ALBERT EINSTEIN

---

Historically, injuries have been treated as isolated cases without consideration of their impact on the body-wide reactions to movement. In Chapter Eleven, beginning on page 169, we discussed the impact on back function from the lower extremities into the back, as well as the shoulder girdle down toward the back.

In this chapter, the knee and shoulder regions are addressed separately to further understand how each are part of the integrated whole. The foot and hip impressively affect the knee. The shoulder complex is largely impacted by everything below it.

Essentially, an injury to each region is actually a full-body injury rather than a local one.

## KNEE ISSUES

We have numerous approaches to strengthen the tissue around the knee, and many of these strategies are helpful. We will not go into detail into the common programs you already know, but will instead cover a few knee rehabilitation, post-rehabilitative, and corrective exercise theories. Due to the numerous maladies affecting the knee, we cannot address each injury or dysfunction, but these are some considerations when contemplating approaches to knee problems.

As the cliché goes, the knee is the dumbest joint in the body, as it depends on the hip and foot and ankle complex to be successful. In the most basic terms, the knee

is comprised of three bones: the tibia, the femur, and the patella. Gary Gray often refers to this complex as a railroad track, with the patella being the train on the track. If the track is not aligned, the train has a rough, bumpy, misaligned ride. When dealing with the knee, our primary objective is to create an environment for the train to successfully ride on the track.

If the hip myofascial tissue of the external rotators is tight, the tight gluteal complex causes external rotation of the hip, and the femur will be externally rotated to the tibia. This is especially true if there is a flat foot involved, as this will cause the tibia to medially rotate. If one track—the femur—rotates *out* and the other track—the tibia—rotates *in,* the patella will not smoothly or efficiently articulate, causing dysfunction and eventually pain.

Before you can implement a strategy for strengthening, you must assess if the femur is laterally rotated on the tibia, or if the tibia is medially rotated on the femur. Likewise, the opposite environment can be the case, with the femur internally rotated to the tibia, or the tibia laterally rotated to the femur.

Determine the scenario by first assessing the foot structure and function. To fully appreciate the nuances of the foot would take anywhere from a chapter to a complete book, and that is not our scope here. However, we still must address the foot and its impact on knee alignment by applying the following concept based on apparent foot structure.

If the foot appears to have a high arch—commonly known as a pes cavus foot—in most cases the tibia will be laterally rotated. Here the calcaneus is relatively inverted as compared to a neutral foot; the talus is in an abducted position, and the tibia will follow these bony landmarks.

Please refer to Photos 12.1, 12.2, and 12.3 showing the relationship of the knee alignment with a cavus-like foot.

Photo 12.1 shows how the knee is in a relative varus position when the foot has a cavus structure. Notice how the tibia is relatively rotated outward.

PHOTO 12.2 SQUAT WITH VARUS FOREFOOT

PHOTO 12.1 CAVUS FOOT STRUCTURE

Photo 12.2 shows a varus knee position during a squat when a person has a cavus foot structure.

Compare the cavus foot to the planus or flat foot and the relation of the knee alignment in the next photos. Photo 12.3 shows how the knee is in a relative valgus position when the foot has a planus structure. Notice how the tibia is relatively rotated inward.

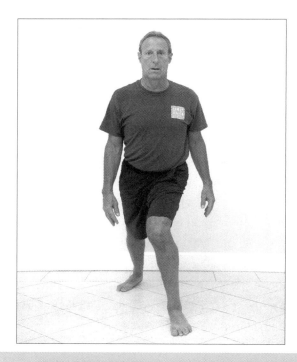

PHOTO 12.3 KNEE ALIGNMENT WITH A PLANUS FOOT STRUCTURE

Compare the cavus foot in Photo 12.3 to this planus or flat foot and the relation of the knee alignment in the Photo 12.4.

**PHOTO 12.4 SQUAT WITH VALGUS KNEE POSITION DUE TO A PLANUS OR FLAT FOOT**

Additionally, the femur will typically rotate outward and the gluteal complex becomes shorter and tighter. As you recall from the *Characteristics of Human Motion* section of Chapter One beginning on page 11, the tissue will eccentrically load before it concentrically unloads.

Most often, people with a cavus foot have shorter and tighter gluteal tissue, which can compromise the ability to optimally load the gluteal complex. When people with this foot structure do a lunge, they have difficulty stabilizing the first ray and metatarsal head.

This is often the result of two issues.

First, the soft tissue of the foot is short and tight, inhibiting the foot in its effort to evert and unload. This causes an inability to eccentrically load the hip and inhibits optimal internal rotation of the femur and tibia.

If this is the case, have the person do a forward sagittal-plane lunge and reach to the opposite side at waist, hip, or knee height depending upon mobility and threshold, shown in Photo 12.6. In this sense, "threshold" refers to the motion the client exhibits before displaying any compensatory movement patterns or possible discomfort.

**PHOTO 12.5 LUNGE WITH VALGUS KNEE AND FOREFOOT**

**PHOTO 12.6 SAGITTAL-PLANE LUNGE WITH OPPOSITE-SIDE LATERAL REACH**

The reach to the opposite side will cause the calcaneus to evert, the forefoot to abduct, the tibia to internally rotate, and the ankle to gain dorsiflexion. Those with this alignment pattern usually feel less discomfort at the patellofemoral joint during this exercise because the medial or opposite lateral reach allows the femur to move farther and faster than the tibia, resulting in better alignment. When this occurs, the tissue can begin to gain strength due to improved range of motion and tissue loading.

On the other hand, in those with a pes planus or flat foot, the calcaneus is everted, the talus is adducted, the tibia medially rotated, and the forefoot is abducted. In many cases, the femur will rotate medially as well. In those cases when the femur is medially rotated, often due to the tight adductor complex, the patella does not track well.

Using the same concepts as mentioned earlier, have the client reach to the same side laterally when performing a sagittal-plane lunge—see Photo 12.7.

**PHOTO 12.7 SAGITTAL-PLANE LUNGE WITH SAME-SIDE LATERAL REACH**

The lateral reach will cause the thoracic spine to rotate toward the same side, and the lumbar spine and hip will follow. When the hip rotates in that direction, the femur and tibia will rotate outward, causing the talus to abduct and the calcaneus to invert. The forefoot will move into relative adduction, and then will move into a relative plantar flexion.

In many cases, these strategies improve patellofemoral tracking and the tissue will have an improved environment to allow proper loading and unloading.

For those afflicted with a knee injury or postsurgery, such as meniscal repair, ACL reconstruction, or knee replacement, there are many protocols and progressions that achieve the same goals and objectives. These range from reducing inflammation and swelling, gaining range of motion, building strength in the soft tissue affecting the knee, and regaining functional strength and optimal thresholds.

Make sure the care, rehabilitation, and strengthening programs not only locally address the knee, but also the foot and ankle complex and the hips. The calf group often becomes very tight in the people who have undergone these injuries and procedures.

Obviously, the mechanics of gait are altered in these scenarios, too. When the knee is injured, flexion and extension are negatively impacted. In most cases, not only is the knee affected, but the ankle also does not move through adequate dorsiflexion, causing the tissue to lose the eccentric loading in the calf.

Under normal gait conditions, when the gastrocnemius is eccentrically loaded, it will cause the knee to extend. However, due to tissue injury around the knee and any subsequent inflammation, the knee is unable to gain that motion, which also negatively affects ankle kinematics. If the ankle is not properly loading and the calf group has become tight, the foot will suffer these negative effects, resulting with the inability to fully pronate the foot structure.

If the foot becomes immobile, there will be a reduced reaction through the leg, limiting movement in the hip. This can also impact the low back, the thoracic spine, the shoulder girdle, and the cervical spine. What was initially a knee injury, now becomes a full-body injury.

Therefore, in those affected by a knee issue, it is critically important to address the mobility of the foot and ankle complex, as well as the hips.

When the knee is injured, especially if surgery is involved, the capsule gets tight. People complain they only have a limited amount of knee flexion, and cannot get past a certain point. Swelling and inflammation usually are the cause of this lack of motion. However, when those issues subside, adhesions resulting from the incisions can still restrict flexion.

When I was going through rehabilitation from a knee replacement, I experienced this. My son Adam, an excellent physical therapist, placed a Mulligan belt around the tibial tuberosity, and then put the belt around his waist as he stood behind me. With the foot of my affected knee on a box, he pushed my hips forward while at the same time pulling backward to create a force from the belt through the tibial tuberosity, driving the tibia backward. This moved the femur forward on the tibia, allowing the knee to glide forward.

Within five minutes, I gained 10 degrees of flexion and was well on my way to progressing easily through rehabilitation. I now often use this technique, seen in Photos 12.8 and 12.9, with those who have had knee surgery or replacement.

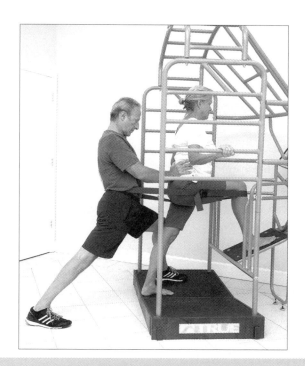

**PHOTO 12.8 KNEE CAPSULE STRETCH, LATERAL VIEW**

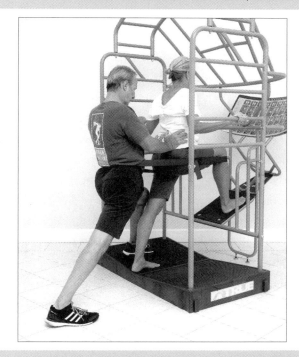

**PHOTO 12.9 KNEE CAPSULE STRETCH, POSTEROLATERAL VIEW**

*Notice the hips are pressed forward while a posterior force is driven through the tibial tuberosity to cause the femur to glide forward on the tibia, which is required for successful knee flexion.*

For your clients who have had ACL reconstruction, do not use this approach until eight to 12 weeks post-op so the graft and anchors are well-healed and calcification around the anchors has taken place. It is prudent to check with the physician to make sure the grafts are fully healed prior to implementing this mobilization. Additionally, you may want to inquire if this is permissible at the facility where you are employed.

We have had excellent results using this technique.

In Appendix Two, page 215, you will find a knee-strengthening progression as an example of the programs we use. You can modify it according to the symptoms, limitations, compensations, and idiosyncrasies of the patient to make the experience a personalized exercise plan.

## SHOULDER ISSUES

Like the knee, there are many good strategies, techniques, and progressions for rehabilitation following shoulder injury or surgery. Historically, treatment and training of the shoulder has been done from an isolated-joint perspective, rather than from a global perspective.

Aside from blunt trauma, in many cases the shoulder joint is not the problematic area, but has been the victim of something else not functioning properly elsewhere in the body. As you know, the shoulder joint is greatly dependent upon scapular movement, which is dependent upon thoracic spine motion, which reacts to the actions of the pelvis, legs, and feet. Clearly, a shoulder injury is a global body issue, not just a local problem.

When a person presents with a shoulder issue, first look at scapular mobility to make sure the scapula is gliding over the ribs. If there is a limitation there, the humeral head runs the risk of impinging the supraspinatus tendon in the acromion process.

During abduction of the humerus, the scapula must abduct and elevate to allow the humeral head to articulate under the acromion process. If the scapula does not optimally glide into abduction and elevation, the risk of impingement increases.

Additionally, check the motion of the clavicle at the sternoclavicular joint, where it should slightly abduct during shoulder abduction. This can become tight, which may adversely impact shoulder-girdle kinematics. This is commonly overlooked.

The scapula is also greatly influenced by the action of the hips. When the same-side hip moves through extension, the scapula reacts by adducting with a slight depression. This creates a conducive environment for shoulder flexion. As the hip flexes, the scapula abducts and slightly elevates, enhancing shoulder extension.

When the same-side hip adducts, the same-side scapula abducts, allowing shoulder abduction. The opposite hip that adducts enhances opposite scapular retraction or adduction. When the opposite hip goes through internal rotation, it creates a successful environment for the opposite shoulder to move through internal rotation, and the same-side shoulder to move into external rotation.

Practice the movements described in the previous paragraphs and sense how the scapula reacts. Alternatively, place your hands on someone's scapula and have the person move through these motions so you can feel the scapular reactions.

You cannot stop with only looking at hip function when reviewing a shoulder issue either. Remember, if a hip is limited in any plane of motion, it tells us a *what*, not a *why*.

When assessing limited shoulder motion, continue looking lower to check the motion and function in the foot and ankle complex. When you assess a person with a shoulder issue, you should also analyze how the foot is reacting. People often present with symptoms of shoulder pain that are actually a result of a foot problem. The majority of overuse injuries in the shoulder are a global problem of movement limitations elsewhere in the body.

Remember to first look globally, and then locally when assessing an injury issue anywhere in the body.

In Appendix Three, beginning on page 217, you will find a shoulder reconditioning and strengthening progression as an example of one of the programs we use. You should modify it according to the symptoms, limitations, compensations, and idiosyncrasies of each client to make the experience a personalized exercise plan.

## COMMON INJURIES AND COMPENSATIONS

Volumes have been written about special-population demographics. The injury issues of the low back, knee, and shoulder are the three leading maladies fitness professionals experience with participants in their fitness programs.

Limitations in the Big Movement Rocks of the foot and ankle complex, hips, and thoracic spine often lead to overuse issues in the lumbar spine, the knee, and the shoulder. The low back is stuck between the hips and the thoracic spine. If either of these regions becomes limited in motion, the lumbar spine often becomes overused in one or more

planes of motion and over time, injury ensues. Of course, if the hips or thoracic spine are limited in movement, we must step back and ask why, and then assess and develop a strategy to correct the limitation.

The knee is between the foot and ankle complex and the hip, which greatly influence the reactive environment of the knee. In many people with a knee issue, you will find the foot or hip is the true culprit negatively impacting the knee.

Likewise, other regions of the body impact the shoulder-girdle complex.

You will need to consider these common compensations when working with other special populations, such as those who are overweight, diabetic, or have a central nervous system dysfunction. These populations often have a compromised gait, and the understanding of human movement can help when developing a movement plan or conditioning program for them.

# CHAPTER THIRTEEN

# USING THESE INSIGHTS IN YOUR WORK

*"You must be in tune with the times and
prepared to break with tradition."*

~ J A M E S   A G E E

---

The chapters of this book have been a career-long and experiential path to things I have seen in practice. A volume of research articles and books I have read and colleagues I have spoken with have contributed to this body of work.

However, you cannot rush time. We have to pay our dues through years of practice and developing theories as we delve into situations, scenarios, and opportunities.

Much of the discussion in this book is not found in research, but is an extrapolation of that research. Many of the scenarios are not peer reviewed, but the symptoms or compensations, idiosyncrasies, and assessment of clients are quite similar.

The approaches used for the corrective strategies and progressions toward the goals and return to activities are reproducible. As discussed in Chapter Nine, *Pre-Programming Insights,* beginning on page 137, when we are able to reproduce these experiences with the same or nearly the same results, there is something to be said about the position or perspective. Sometimes we get lucky. Sometimes, when luck hits more than once with similar results, that is an "aha" moment.

There are no bad exercises. The exercises are "bad" based on the limitations, compensations, and idiosyncrasies of each person. We must learn who our clients are, how they move, and how they like to be coached. When we learn about them, we can better serve them.

Study and understand the research, books, seminars, and certifications as much as possible. Understand the

normative data, but realize your client is an individual and may not fit into common demographics. Look at and treat your client as that individual and do not compare one person to anyone else. As Gary Gray often says, "Compare you to you," not to others in a demographic profile.

The various concepts, movement issues, and processes described in this book have worked and will continue to do so. There may be a frustrating aspect of certain cases, and strategic approaches may not always work. That is when personal trainers or health and fitness professionals must step back and refer to the principles and concepts before implementing new applications.

According to the dictionary, "principles" are *the fundamental truths or propositions that serves a system of belief or behavior or for a chain of reasoning.* These principles will never change, as many of them are based on the natural laws of gravity, ground-reaction forces, mass, momentum, bodyweight, three-dimensional environments, and integration.

"Concepts" are *abstract ideas or general notions based on principles.*

"Applications" are *the strategies implemented based on the truths of movement, how the clients move, and the concepts observed over your career.*

Be persistent, be patient, and be creative. Develop a strong philosophy based on the principles, concepts, and applications you have observed over time.

Do not be a slave to exercise equipment. Do not be so entrenched in certain exercises or movement patterns that you lose objectivity and creativity. Do not become so stuck into a mindset or system that you refuse to recognize any other approach to movement or programming.

Develop a toolbox mentality that serves all populations from the injured and compromised, to the sedentary, to the general fitness and apparently healthy client, to the athletic population.

Have a rationale of why you are using an exercise tool or movement pattern. Be sure that rationale is based on the principles (truths), concepts (notions), and strategies of application.

Network with professionals such as doctors, physical therapists, chiropractors, massage therapists, dietitians, athletic trainers, strength and conditioning coaches, and other personal trainers. We are not islands unto ourselves, but a network able to assist in the health and wellbeing of those we serve.

If you embrace some of this book's content and philosophies, develop a caring, nurturing environment for your clients, you will be successful. After all, isn't that why we are in this field?

Good luck and good health!

*Chuck Wolf*

# A P P E N D I C E S   L I S T

## APPENDIX ONE

*OVERVIEW OF THE SIX FLEXIBILITY HIGHWAYS*

## APPENDIX TWO

*HIP AND KNEE STRENGTHENING PROGRESSION*

## APPENDIX THREE

*SHOULDER RECONDITIONING PROGRESSION*

## APPENDIX FOUR

*REFERENCES*

## APPENDIX FIVE

*HUMAN MOTION ASSOCIATES HEALTH HISTORY*

# APPENDIX ONE

# OVERVIEW OF THE SIX FLEXIBILITY HIGHWAYS

## THE ANTERIOR FLEXIBILITY HIGHWAY

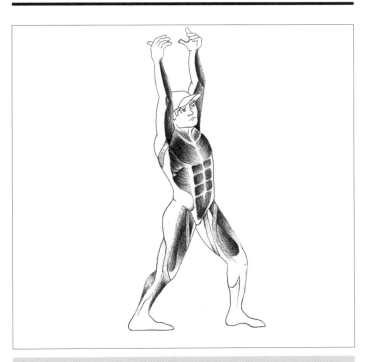

FIGURE A1.1 ANTERIOR FLEXIBILITY HIGHWAY

### KEY INTERSECTIONS

- *Anterior tibialis to distal quads*
- *Proximal quads to distal hip flexor*
- *Proximal hip flexor to distal abdominals*
- *Proximal abdominals to distal pectorals*
- *Proximal pectorals to distal delts*
- *Opposite obliques to opposite shoulder*

### *STRETCHING THE ANTERIOR FLEXIBILITY HIGHWAY*

LEVEL 1　　　　　LEVEL 2

PHOTO A1.1A AND B STRETCHING THE ANTERIOR FLEXIBILITY HIGHWAY

The Anterior Flexibility Highway runs from the south to the north—the bottom to the top of the body—or along the sagittal plane with flexion and extension movements occurring on this Highway.

The myofascial tissues of this Highway begin at the dorsal surface of the foot with the toe extensors, and interchange with the anterior compartment of the ankle and tibia. This runs from the anterior tibialis north, connecting to the distal quadriceps near the patellar tendon.

The next interchange north is the patellar tendon and the quadriceps attachment northward to the hip flexors. To enhance function of both the quadriceps and hip flexors, it is important to lengthen both structures together.

The hip flexors intersect with the abdominals that travel to the ribs, sternum, and the sternochondral fascia, and venture into the pectorals, anterior shoulder, and the sternocleidomastoid.

From there, an angular detour takes our journey to the mastoid process of the Anterior Flexibility Highway, which enhances extension moments.

## POSTERIOR FLEXIBILITY HIGHWAY

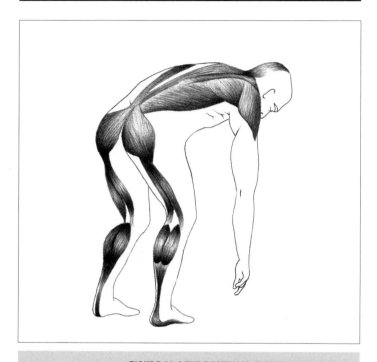

**FIGURE A1.2 THE POSTERIOR FLEXIBILITY HIGHWAY**

### KEY INTERSECTIONS

- *Plantar fascia to calcaneus to Achilles*
- *Posterior calf to distal hams*
- *Proximal hams to distal glutes*
- *Proximal glutes to distal erector spinae*
- *Opposite glutes and lats*
- *Distal erector spinae to occipital to epicranial fascia*

### *STRETCHING THE POSTERIOR FLEXIBILITY HIGHWAY*

**PHOTO A1.2 STRETCHING THE POSTERIOR FLEXIBILITY HIGHWAY**

The Posterior Flexibility Highway runs from the south to the north or along the sagittal plane with flexion movements occurring on this highway. The myofascia of this highway begins at the plantar surface of the foot from the toe flexors, moves through the posterior compartment of the ankle, and meets at the Achilles tendon. Through the posterior calf group of the gastrocnemius, soleus, and posterior tibialis northward, the knee interchange meets the hamstrings.

The gastrocnemius attaches at the femoral condyles and conjoins with the descending hamstrings that attach at the tibial condyles. In fact, the gastrocnemius and hamstrings connect with each other, forming the "trapeze artists of the body."

The hamstrings attach below and around the knee on the tibial condyles. The hamstrings run north, attaching at the ischial tuberosity, and merging into the sacrotuberous ligament. In this region, a major interchange emerges as the sacrotuberous ligament meets the lumbosacral fascia, and passes into the gluteal complex, as well as the erector spinae.

The erector group travels north to connect with the occiput and conjoins with the epicranial fascia to the forehead.

It is important to stretch the union of the gluteals and the erector spinae musculature in an integrated fashion, as any functional lumbar movement pattern includes the gluteals. The relationship of these structures should be developed together.

The final posterior journey terminates at the scalp fascia.

# LATERAL FLEXIBILITY HIGHWAY

**FIGURE A1.3 THE LATERAL FLEXIBILITY HIGHWAY**

## *KEY INTERSECTIONS*

- *Peroneals to ITB and TFL*
- *ITB and TFL to lateral gluteals*
- *Lateral gluteals to QL and obliques*
- *Obliques to opposite pectorals and shoulder*

## *STRETCHING LATERAL FLEXIBILITY HIGHWAY*

**PHOTO A1.3 STRETCHING THE LATERAL FLEXIBILITY HIGHWAY**

The Lateral Flexibility Highway is commonly overlooked in discussions on function. The Lateral Flexibility Highway runs from the south to the north along the frontal plane with abduction and adduction movements occurring along this line.

Running from the lateral ankle and the peroneal group, the Lateral Highway goes north to the lateral tibial condyle and the iliotibial band. Moving upward from this taut structure, the IT band merges with the tensor fascia lata, the gluteus medius and minimus, and then meets with the gluteus maximus.

When analyzing the multidirectional fibrous "routes" of the gluteal complex, we know to include these sections of the Highways with all Flexibility Highway stretching. The gluteals are the "command central" of our center of gravity, balance, and power. They are used in all functional movement patterns, and thus are the hub of tri-plane movement patterns.

Along the Lateral Flexibility Highway, the lateral gluteals are adjacent to the QL and then the obliques.

The obliques merge with the external and internal intercostals toward the anterior aspect and the latissimus dorsi in the posterior aspect. Additionally, these structures are close neighbors to the transverse abdominis by way of fascial anatomy.

From this point north, the lats will meet up with the posterior rotator cuff. There is a bypass at the junction of the latissimus dorsi and the trapezius group, whereby the journey northbound traverses through the trapezius group to the sternocleidomastoid.

## THE ANTERIOR X-FACTOR

**FIGURE A1.4 THE ANTERIOR X-FACTOR**

### KEY INTERSECTIONS

- *Opposite adductor to pubic ramus*
- *Pubic ramus to opposite obliques*
- *Obliques to serratus anterior to pectorals*
- *Pectorals to the shoulder*

### STRETCHING THE ANTERIOR X-FACTOR

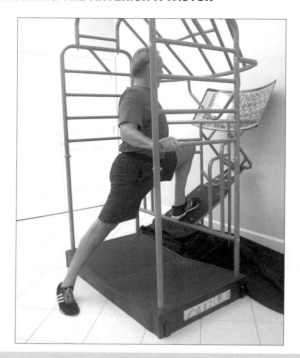

**PHOTO A1.4 STRETCHING THE ANTERIOR X-FACTOR**

All motions involving rotation and extension run along the Anterior X-Factor (AXF). When viewing the anatomy of the adductors to the opposite pectoral and shoulder region, there is a somewhat parallel line along these tissues. This Flexibility Highway runs from the adductor insertion on the linea aspera on the posterior femur and originates at the pubic ramus on the pelvis.

At this point, there is a close fascial relationship between the origin of the adductors to the rectus abdominis as it traverses along the abdominals to the opposite intercostals and obliques, upward to the serratus anterior, into the pectorals, and into the opposite shoulder complex. Therefore, any motion that involves extension and rotation of the opposite side runs along the AXF.

Additionally, when we abduct and extend an arm, similar to a throwing motion or a golfer's backswing, the tissue from the deltoid into the biceps and forearm is included in the AXF.

It is crucial to possess ample mobility in the adductors, abdominals, and pectoral regions to enhance motions through the AXF.

Likewise, it is important to maintain good range of motion in the hamstrings, as these tissues are the neighbor of the adductors, and highly affect them.

# POSTERIOR X-FACTOR

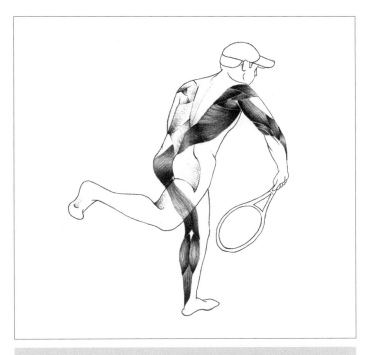

**FIGURE A1.5 THE POSTERIOR X-FACTOR**

### KEY INTERSECTIONS

- *Calf to hamstrings*
- *Hamstrings to gluteals to sacrotuberous ligament to lumbar fascia*
- *Lumbar fascia to opposite latissimus dorsi to the shoulder*

## STRETCHING THE POSTERIOR X-FACTOR

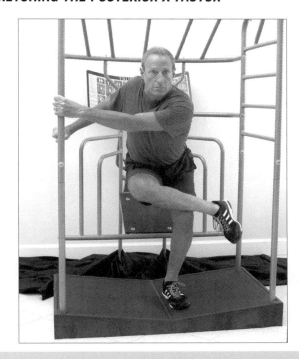

**PHOTO A1.5 STRETCHING THE POSTERIOR X-FACTOR**

As you view the posterior architecture of the soft tissue, the Posterior X-Factor (PXF), notice the nearly parallel line between the opposite gluteal complex and the latissimus dorsi. Both tissues entwine into the lumbosacral fascia, thereby joining the opposite hip and shoulder.

The importance of the PXF comes into play during flexion and rotational actions, such as the follow-through in a throw, the backswing during a golf swing, tennis swing follow-through, or simply picking up an object within reach and lateral to you.

# THE TURNPIKE

## KEY INTERSECTIONS

- *Scalenes and cervicis capitis to the opposite rhomboid*
- *Rhomboid to subscapularis to serratus anterior*
- *Serratus anterior to external oblique to the opposite hip*

## STRETCHING THE TURNPIKE

**PHOTOS A1.6 A AND B STRETCHING THE TURNPIKE**

This unique Highway system forms a relationship with the cervical spine and the hip via the opposite shoulder girdle. Running from the opposite scalene and capitis cervicis, these tissues conjoin with the rhomboids on the same side. The rhomboids attach to both scapulae, but due to the angulation of the rhomboid, these tissues attach to the opposite scapula. The rhomboid runs laterally to connect with the subscapularis approximately one-third from the medial border.

The subscapularis travels laterally to merge with the serratus anterior about 20 percent from the lateral border. The serratus anterior wraps around the side of the body, connecting with the pectorals and external obliques.

The external oblique runs on an angle toward the linea alba of the rectus abdominis to the opposite hip. This "turnpike" creates the indirect attachment from the same-side posterior cervical spine to the opposite shoulder, and diagonally back to the same-side hip on the anterior side.

## APPENDIX TWO

# HIP AND KNEE-STRENGTHENING PROGRESSION

This hip and knee reconditioning program is a progression we often use at Human Motion Associates. These are some of the movement patterns, but we may change the order, intensity, number of reps and sets, and program objectives to suit a client's needs.

If a client presents with an injury, we get medical clearance prior to commencing any form of treatment or corrective exercises.

After a client was in physical therapy and subsequently discharged, we may be able to start from a later stage than at the beginning of the program. This program is only listed as an example and should be modified based on the condition, goals, objectives, and medical history of each client.

Programming for hip and knee strengthening is highly variable, with unlimited exercise choices. These are just a sample of the many movements we use when working with our various populations.

The key issues we watch for is the quality of movement, particularly in the foot and ankle complex and hips.

| | OBJECTIVE | SETS | REPS | GOAL |
| --- | --- | --- | --- | --- |
| *SUPINE STRAIGHT-LEG RAISES* | Acute Rehabilitation | 2 | 8 | 3 sets of 15 reps |
| *PRONE STRAIGHT-LEG HIP EXTENSION* | Acute Rehabilitation | 2 | 8 | 3 sets of 15 reps |
| *TRI-PLANE SHIFTING PATTERNS* | Mobilization | 2 | 5 | 3 sets of 15 reps |
| *FRONTAL-PLANE SHIFTING PATTERNS* | Strength and Mobility | 2 | 5 | 3 sets of 15 reps |
| *ANKLE MOBES* | Mobilization | 2 | 8 | 3 sets of 15 reps |
| *WALL PATTERNS* | Mobility | 2 | 5 | 3 sets of 10 reps in each vector |
| *WALL BANGERS* | Remedial Integrated Strength | 2 | 5 | 3 sets of 15 reps |
| *STEP-UPS—SAGITTAL PLANE* | Integrated Strength | 2 | 5 | 3 sets of 15 reps |
| *STEP-UPS—FRONTAL PLANE* | Integrated Strength | 2 | 5 | 3 sets of 15 reps |
| *TRI-PLANE LUNGES* | Integrated Strength | 2 | 5 | 3 sets of 10 reps |
| *TRI-PLANE LUNGES TO STEP-UPS* | Integrated Strength | 2 | 10 | 3 sets of 10 reps |

| | OBJECTIVE | SETS | REPS | GOAL |
|---|---|---|---|---|
| **GOBLET SQUATS** | Integrated Strength | 2 | 10 | Variable depending upon client needs |
| **ASYMMETRICAL GOBLET SQUATS** | Integrated Strength | 2 | 3 | 3 sets of 8 reps each direction |
| **SINGLE-LEG SQUATS** | Integrated Strength | 2 | 10 | 3 sets of 15 reps |
| **SCISSOR SQUATS** | Explosiveness | 2 | 10 | 3 sets of 12 reps |
| **SINGLE-LEG BOUNDS** | Explosiveness | 2 | 10 | 3 sets of 12 reps |
| **TRI-PLANE HOPS** | Explosiveness | 2 | 10 | 3 sets of 12 reps |
| **MEDBALL JUMP TOSS** | Explosiveness | 2 | 10 | 3 sets of 12 reps |

# SHOULDER RECONDITIONING PROGRESSION

This shoulder reconditioning program is a progression we use at Human Motion Associates.

If a client presents with an injury, we get medical clearance prior to commencing any form of treatment or corrective exercises.

If the client was in physical therapy and has since been discharged, we may be able to start from a later stage than at the beginning of the program. This program is only listed as an example and should be modified based on the condition, goals, objectives, and medical history of the client.

| | OBJECTIVE | SETS | REPS | GOAL |
|---|---|---|---|---|
| *RELATIVE SHOULDER MOTION— SAGITTAL-PLANE SCAPULAR MOBILITY* | Mobilization | 2 | 5 | 3 sets of 15 reps |
| *RELATIVE SHOULDER MOTION— FRONTAL-PLANE SCAPULAR MOBILITY* | Mobilization | 2 | 5 | 3 sets of 15 reps |
| *RELATIVE SHOULDER MOTION— TRANSVERSE-PLANE SCAPULAR MOBILITY* | Mobilization | 2 | 5 | 3 sets of 15 reps |
| *D1/D2 PATTERNS* | Strength and Mobility | 2 | 5 | 3 sets of 15 reps |
| *WALL PATTERNS* | Mobility | 2 | 5 | 3 sets of 10 reps each vector |
| *HUGHSTON EXERCISES* | Isolated Strength | 2 | 10 | 3 sets of 15 reps |
| *JOBES EXERCISE* | Isolated Strength | 2 | 10 | 3 sets of 15 reps |
| *SHOULDER EXTENSION WITH EXTERNAL ROTATION* | Isolated Strength | 2 | 10 | 3 sets of 15 reps |
| *ISOLATED TO INTEGRATED INTERNAL ROTATION* | Integrated Strength | 2 | 10 | 3 sets of 15 reps |

| | OBJECTIVE | SETS | REPS | GOAL |
|---|---|---|---|---|
| ISOLATED TO INTEGRATED EXTERNAL ROTATION | Integrated Strength | 2 | 10 | 3 sets of 15 reps |
| BOX STABILITY | Integrated Strength | 2 | 10 | 3 sets of 15 reps |
| STABILITY BALL PLANK WITH VIBRATION | Integrated Strength | 2 | 30 seconds | 3-5 sets at 60 seconds |
| FLEX BAR OR BODY BLADE | Integrated Strength | 2 | 10 | 3 sets of 15 reps |
| SHOULDER PRESS | Isolated Strength | 2 | 10 | 3 sets of 15 reps |
| TRIANGULATED SHOULDER PRESS | Integrated Strength | 2 | 2 | 3 sets of 3 reps each vector |
| WARDING PATTERNS | Integrated Strength | 2 | 30 seconds | 3-5 sets at 60 seconds |

# REFERENCES

Barr K.P., Griggs M., Cadby T., "Lumbar Stabilization: A Review of Core Concepts and Current Literature, Part 1," *American Journal of Physical Medicine and Rehabilitation,* 2005, June; 84(6): 473-480

Barr K.P., Griggs M., Cadby T., "Lumbar Stabilization: A Review of Core Concepts and Current Literature, Part 2," *American Journal of Physical Medicine and Rehabilitation,* 2005, June; 86 (1) 72-80

Bompa, Tudor O., PhD, *Periodization Training for Sports,* Human Kinetics, 1999

Carlsoo, Sven, *How Man Moves,* 1972, London, William Heinemann Ltd.

Clark, M.A., "Integrated Flexibility Training," Thousand Oaks, CA, National Academy of Sports Medicine, 2001

Chu, Donald A, *Jumping Into Plyometrics,* Leisure Press, 1992

Dykyj, Daria, PhD, "Anatomy of Motion," Clinics in Podiatric Medicine and Surgery, July 1988, Vol. 5, No. 3

Earls, James, *Born to Walk Myofascial Efficiency and the Body in Movement,* Lotus Publishing, 2014

Fairclough J, Hayashi K, Toumi H, Lyons K, Bydder G, Phillips N, Best TM, Benjamin M, "The Functional Anatomy of The Iliotibial Band During Flexion and Extension of The Knee: Implications for Understanding Iliotibial Band Syndrome," *Journal of Anatomy* (2006) 208, pp. 309-316

Fredericson, M, Wolf, C, "Iliotibial Band Syndrome in Runners: Innovations in Treatment," *American Journal of Sports Medicine,* 2005 May-June:24 35, 451-459

Gottschalk F, Kourosh S, Leveau B, "The Functional Anatomy of Tensor Fasciae Lata and Gluteus Medius and Minimus," *Journal of Anatomy* (1989), pp. 179-189

Gracovetsky, Serge, PhD, "The Spinal Engine," 2008

Gracovetsky, Serge, PhD, "Is the Lumbodorsal Fascia Necessary?," *Journal of Bodywork and Movement Therapies* (2008) 12, 194-197, Elsevier

Gray, Gary, PT, "Pronation and Supination," Wynn Marketing, Adrian, MI, 2001

Gray, Gary, PT, "Functional Biomechanics: Pure Definitions," Wynn Marketing, Adrian, MI, 2001

Hodges, P, van den Hoorn, W, Dawson, A, Cholewicki, J, "Changes in the Mechanical Properties of the Trunk in Low Back Pain May Be Associated with Recurrence," *Journal of Biomechanics,* 01/2009; 42(1):61-6

Inman, Verne, *Human Walking,* Williams & Wilkins, 1981

Intension Designs, Biotensegrity, *intensiondesigns.com*

Ishikawa, Masaki, Komi, Paavo, "Muscle Fascicle and Tendon Behavior During Human Locomotion Revisited," *Exercise and Science Reviews,* ACSM, Volume 36, Number 4, October, 2008

Itoh, Kazunori, Okada, Kaoru, Kawakita, Kenji, "A Proposed Experimental Model of Myofascial Trigger Points in Human Muscle after Slow Eccentric Exercise," *Acupuncture in Medicine* 2004; 22(1): 2-13

Katch, Frank, Katch, Victor L, McArdle, William D., *Exercise Physiology: Energy, Nutrition, and Human Performance,* 1986, Philadelphia, Lea & Febiger

Latash, Mark, Scholz, John, Schoner, Gregor, "Motor Control Strategies Revealed in the Structure of Motor Variability," *Exercise and Science Reviews,* Volume 30, Number 1, January, 2002

Latash, Mark "The Bliss of Motor Abundance," *Experimental Brain Research,* 2012, March; 217 (1): 1-5

Marshall, Paul W. M., McKee, Amanda, Murphy, Bernadette A., "Impaired Trunk and Ankle Stability in Subjects with Functional Ankle Instability," *Medicine & Science In Sports & Exercise,* Vol. 41, No. 8, pp.1549-1557

Masi, A, Nair, K, Evans, T, Yousef, G, "Clinical, Biomechanical, and Physiological Translational Interpretations of Human Being Myofascial Tone or Tension," *International Journal of Therapeutic Massage and Bodywork,* Vol. 3, No. 4, December, 2010.

Masson, Dr. Robert, Neurospine Institute, Ocoee, FL., *Neurospineinstitute.org*

McGill, Stuart, *Low Back Disorders: Evidenced-Based Prevention and Rehabilitation,* Human Kinetics

Muller, Divo, Schleip, Robert, "Facial Fitness: Fascia Oriented Training for Bodywork and Movement Therapies," *Terra Rosa e-magazine,* Issue No. 7

Myers, Thomas, *Anatomy Trains, 3rd Edition,* Churchill, Livingstone, Elsevier, 2014

Myers, Thomas, *The Anatomist's Corner,* Kinesis, Inc., 2016

National Academy of Sports Medicine, *Lower Body Muscular Anatomy,* 2000

National Academy of Sports Medicine, *Upper Body Muscular Anatomy,* 2000

Neumann, Donald, *Kinesiology of the Musculoskeletal System: Foundations for Physical Rehabilitation,* Mosby, 2002

Powers, Scott K, Howley, Edward T, Exercise Physiology: *Theory and Application to Fitness and Performance,* 1990, Dubuque, IA, Wm. C. Brown Publishers

Prestige Cervical Core Education Course, Medtronics, 2007

Rolf, Ida P, PhD, *Rolfing: Reestablishing the Natural Alignment and Structural Integration of the Human Body for Vitality and Well-Being*, Healing Arts Press, 1989

Sahrmann, Shirley, *Diagnosis and Treatment of Movement Impairment Syndromes*, Mosby, 2002

Santos, M, McIntire, K, Foecking, J, Liu, W, "The Effects of Ankle Bracing on Motion of The Knee and The Hip Joint during Trunk Rotation Tasks," *Clinical Biomechanics* 19 (2004) 964-971, Elsevier

Scarr, Graham, *Biotensegrity The Structural Basis of Life*, Handspring Publishing, 2014

Schamberger, Wolf, *The Malalignment Syndrome*, Churchill Livingstone, 2002

Schleip, Robert, Findley, Thomas W., Chaitow, Leon, Huijing, Peter A., *Fascia: The Tensional Network of the Human Body*, Churchill, Livingstone, Elsevier, 2012

Schleip, Robert et al, *Fascia in Sport and Movement*, Handspring Publishing, 2015

Schleip, Robert, Findley, Thomas W, Chaitow, Leon, Huijing, Peter A, Fascia Connective Tissues: Scientific Foundation and Suggested Practical Applications," *Journal of Bodywork and Movement Therapies,* 2012 xx 1-13

Schleip Robert, Naylor Ian L., Ursu Danie, Melzer Werner, Zorn Adjo, Wilke Hans-Joachim, Lehmann-Horn Frank, Klingler Werner, "Passive Muscle Stiffness May Be Influenced by Active Contractility of Intramuscular Connective Tissue," *Medical Hypotheses,* 2006; 66: 66-71

Schleip, Robert, "Fascial Plasticity—A New Neurobiological Explanation, Part 2," *Journal of Bodywork and Movement Therapies,* April, 2003

Schelip, R., Klinger, W., Lehmann-Horn, F., "Fascia Is Able to Contract in a Smooth Muscle-like Manner and Thereby Influence Musculoskeletal Mechanics," 5th World Congress of Biomechanics, Munich, Germany, July 29-August 4, 2006

Schelip, R., Klinger, W., Lehmann-Horn, F., "Active Contraction of the Thoracolumbar Fascia—Indications of a New Factor in Low Back Pain Research with Implications for Manual Therapy," 5th Interdisciplinary World Congress on Low Back and Pelvic Pain, Melbourne, November, 2004

Schultz, R Louis, PhD, Feitis, Rosemary, DO, *The Endless Web Fascial Anatomy and Physical Reality*, North Atlantic Books, 1996

Simon, S R, Mann, R A, Hagy, J L, Larsen, L J, "Role of the Posterior Calf Muscles in Normal Gait," *Journal of Bone and Joint Surgery,* June 1978, Vol. 60-A, No. 4

Stecco, Antonio, Macchi, Veronica, Stecco, Carla, Porzionato, Andrea, Day, Julie Ann, Delmas, Vincent, De Caro, Raffaele, "Anatomical Study of The Myofascial Continuity in The Anterior Region of The Upper Extremity," *Journal of Bodywork and Movement Therapy,* (2007), April, 27, 2007

Tiberio, David, "Pathomechanics of Structural Foot Deformities," *Journal of the American Physical Therapy Association,* 1988; 68: 1840-1849

Zorn, Adjo, Schmitt, Franz-Josef, Hodeck, Kai Frederich, Schleip, Robert, Weckend, Frank, Klingler, Werner, "The Spring-Like Function of The Lumbar Fascia in Human Walking," *researchgate.net/publications/200796932*

# HUMAN MOTION ASSOCIATES HEALTH HISTORY

## HEALTH PROFILE

Please answer the following questions carefully and thoughtfully. Where additional information is requested, please provide it on the lines provided. All information will be kept confidential.

NAME_____ DATE_____

DATE OF BIRTH_____AGE_____ ☐ MALE ☐ FEMALE ARE YOU PREGNANT? ☐ YES ☐ NO

OCCUPATION_____DUE DATE IF PREGNANT_____

*Are you presently under the care of a physician?* ☐ *Yes* ☐ *No*

*If yes, please explain:* _____

_____

*Physician name, address, phone number:* _____

_____

Date of last physical examination: _____

*Are you presently taking any prescription or non-prescription medications?* ☐ *Yes* ☐ *No*

*If yes, please* _____

_____

*Do you smoke or use smokeless tobacco?* ☐ *Yes* ☐ *No*

*If yes, please complete: If no, have you ever smoked or used smokeless tobacco:* ☐ *Yes* ☐ *No*

_____ *How long? If yes, when did you quit?*_____

_____ *#of Cigarettes per day?*

_____ *#Cigars per day?*

_____ *Pipe per day?*

_____ *Snuff/chewing tobacco, times per day*

*Are you exposed to secondhand smoke at home or in the work place:* ☐ *Yes* ☐ *No*

*What was your last blood cholesterol (total)?* _____ *Last HDL cholesterol (if known)*_____

## PLEASE CHECK AND DATE IF APPLICABLE

☐ *Heart Attack* *Date:* _____ ☐ *Pacemaker* *Date:* _____

☐ *Coronary Valve Surgery Date:* _____ ☐ *Congestive Heart Failure Date:* _____

☐ *Coronary Valve Surgery Date:* _____ ☐ *Stroke Date:* _____

☐ *Angioplasty* *Date:* _____ ☐ *Blood Transfusion(s) Date:* _____

**PLEASE CHECK IF APPLICABLE**

- ☐ Rheumatic Fever
- ☐ Dizziness, Light Headedness, Faintness
- ☐ Chronic Headaches
- ☐ Varicose Veins
- ☐ Hernia
- ☐ Gout
- ☐ Swelling of Feet or Ankles
- ☐ Shortness of Breath
- ☐ At Rest
- ☐ With Activity
- ☐ Cancer

- ☐ Diagnosed Osteoporosis
- ☐ Angina
- ☐ Irregular Heartbeats
- ☐ Palpitations
- ☐ High Blood Pressure
- ☐ Kidney Disease
- ☐ Chronic Cough
- ☐ Productive
- ☐ Non-Productive
- ☐ Seizures

- ☐ Diabetes
- ☐ Heart Murmur
- ☐ Excessive Urination
- ☐ Anemia
- ☐ Thyroid Disorder
- ☐ Lung Disease
- ☐ Chest Pain
- ☐ Arthritis
- ☐ Episodes of Weakness or
- ☐ Paralysis of Body Parts
- ☐ Exercise or Cold–induced

☐ BackPain-Explain:_____

_____

☐ Injuries-Explain:_____

_____

☐ Surgeries-Explain:_____

_____

☐ Other-Explain:_____

_____

# FAMILY HISTORY

Is your father living?  ☐   Yes  ☐   No  ☐   If no, what was his cause of death? _____

_____

Age at death: _____ If yes, how old is he? _____

Please list any of his known medical problems _____

_____

Is your mother living?  ☐   Yes  ☐   No  ☐   If no, what was her cause of death? _____

_____

Age at death: _____ If yes, how old is she? _____

Please list any of her medical problems _____

**Please check here if there is a family history** (*grandparents, brothers, sisters, etc.*) **of:**

# RELATIONSHIP

- ☐ Heart Disease or heart attacks under 55 years old      _____
- ☐ High Blood Pressure      _____
- ☐ Diabetes   _____
- ☐ Stroke   _____
- ☐ Cancer   _____

# EXERCISE

How many days per week do you exercise? _____ How many minutes each session? _____

Please check the exercises you prefer below

- ☐ Walking
- ☐ Stationary Bike
- ☐ Stair Climber
- ☐ Elliptical X-Trainer
- ☐ Aerobics

- ☐ Jogging/Running
- ☐ Regular Bike
- ☐ Yoga/Tai Chi
- ☐ Weight Machines
- ☐ Calisthenics

- ☐ Treadmill Running
- ☐ Free Weights
- ☐ Rowing Machine
- ☐ Weight Training
- ☐ Other _____

I have reviewed and answered each question to the best of my knowledge.

I authorize the release of this information to my primary physician(s). Information will not be released without my written consent. However, the questionnaire information may be used for statistical and/or scientific studies with my right of privacy retained.

Signature _____ Print Name _____

Date_____

# DEDICATION

I have been blessed with many wonderful experiences in my career of 37 years. I could not have had them without the support of many people who have influenced my life. First, my parents, the most loving people, who have set the example to respect others as well as myself. My mother set the tone that family is first and she showed us how to love, share, and have empathy for others.

My father had the highest drive and strongest mindset I have ever known and taught me to work hard, yet respect others. His credo "You only get out of something what you put into it" still resonates within me today. That was my drive in sports and is still a philosophy I live by. I often think of him and hope I can be as driven and as wonderful a dad to my kids as he was to me. I love you, Mom and Dad, and miss you both so much.

My sister has always been a strong supporter, confidant, and sounding board for me. Thank you, Susie, for your support and continuing the strong sense of family Mom has instilled in us. My brother, Stephen, has been the most perfect big brother anyone could ask for. Stephen is a professor of English literature and composition in New York City. I have always admired his command of the English language through his writings. Thank you, my brother, for all your assistance in editing my efforts in this book.

The greatest support I receive is from my beautiful wife Lauren, the love of my life for the last 37 years. She is my driving force, my reason to succeed, and the strength to keep me moving forward during challenging times. Thank you for your love, patience, and assistance all these years. I love you more today than yesterday, but not as much as the many tomorrows.

Along with my wife, my pride and joy are my four beautiful children. Adam, a physical therapist, is one of the most gifted in his field. My daughter Jill, a clinical social worker, amazes me with her knowledge in the fields of hepatitis C, as well as understanding the psychosocial aspects of human behavior. Brittany, an attorney, has an incredible gift of understanding the law and is a strong-minded, logical woman. Kimberly is my sensitive, loving soul who graduated from physical therapy school in May 2017. She has a grasp of human movement like no other I have seen at her young tenure in the business. Thank you all for being my babies. And my babies have given me two beautiful grandchildren, Alexia and Elijah—thank you, Adam. Also, welcome David and Darnell to our family. You are wonderful young men.

There are so many colleagues who have had a strong influence in my career. However, two of the strongest influencers were Mickey and Hazel Gitlitz for giving me my first opportunity in this field. They were the owners of Multiplex in Deerfield, Illinois, where I was an exercise physiologist. They showed me that I could run a successful business, yet make all the staff feel like family. However, if it were not for my first interview with the then-manager of Multiplex, Dawn Norman, I would not have had that great opportunity in that wonderful facility. Dawn is still one of the most intuitive, intelligent people I know in the business.

Other influential professionals who have impacted my career include the late Dr. Wally Salzman. His wisdom and empathy gave me an understanding and awareness of the medical interactions that provided me a better perspective of indications and contraindications of exercise and movement on our anatomical and physiological systems.

Likewise, the guidance and medical advice I have received from Dr. Robert Masson, the leading neurosurgeon in the country, has advanced my understanding of the mechanics of the spine and the influence of movement upon it. Dr. Michael Ray, Dr. Randy Schwartzberg, Dr. Amit Varma, and Dr. Daryl Osbahr, I cannot thank you enough for your wisdom from an orthopedic standpoint that allows me to apply movement and see how it impacts the healing process in various orthopedic medical models. Also, thanks goes to Robert Duggan, DPM, and Curtis Wagner, DPM, as their wisdom has helped me appreciate the function of the foot.

A major impact upon my career was back in the mid-'90s in Detroit, Michigan, when I attended a most fascinating seminar by Gary Gray. I remember waiting to be seated in the hotel restaurant when he and David Tiberio walked in and invited me to join them for dinner. Thank you both for allowing me to join you that evening and especially for your continuing friendship since that day.

My emergence on the speaking circuit began in the late '90s when Peter and Kathy Davis, founders and owners of IDEA, allowed me to present at one of their regional conferences in New York City. Without them, I would not have known that I could present my concepts to the fitness business. Also, thank you, Aprile Peishel, events director for IDEA, for allowing me to present at IDEA events for these many years. More importantly, thank you, Aprile, for your support and friendship.

There are two gentlemen in the industry whom I frequently refer to as the giants when it comes to having a pulse of the industry and knowing nearly all the major players in the fitness, sports performance, and rehabilitation business. They are Chris Poirier, the general manager of Perform Better, and Richard Boyd, former president of PTontheNET, and formerly the vice president of 24-Hour Fitness. Both of these gentlemen gave me opportunities to speak on the largest national and international stages. Both are dear friends for whom I have the deepest gratitude.

Lastly, but definitely not least, thank you to my dear friends and fellow presenters who have shared their insights and perspectives and are some of the brightest minds in the fitness world. Michol Dalcourt, Ian O'Dwyer, Lenny Parracino, Greg Roskopf, Anthony Carey, Gray Cook, Bobby Cappucio, Rodney Corn, Annette Lang, Geralynn Coopersmith, and many others. Thank you for your friendship and help in shaping the fitness industry.

Thank you to Laree Draper of On Target Publications for giving me the opportunity and for her confidence in publishing this book. I am extremely grateful for your patience, suggestions, and coaxing of me to bring out more information to make this book more complete. Thanks also for the encouragement when the work felt like it was starting to become overwhelming! Additionally, special thanks to Jessica Simms, an outstanding artist who had the skill to create the illustrations in this book and the patience to handle my changes.

This book would not be written if it were not for the thousands of attendees of my seminars who encouraged and supported me all these years, many of whom suggested I write a book. A huge gratitude goes to the thousands of clients and patients who allowed me into their lives and were the "living labs" for me to try new techniques and emerge with perspectives that have influenced my career, and hopefully helped them feel better. Thank you for your confidence and permitting me to do so.

Hopefully through this journey, I have made a difference in the lives I have served. I hope you find this book useful in your career.

In health,

Chuck

# Index